Gold Stars®

Maths

AGES
7-9
Key Stage 2

This edition published by Parragon Books Ltd in 2014

Parragon Books Ltd
Chartist House
15–17 Trim Street
Bath BA1 1HA, UK
www.parragon.com

Written by Paul Broadbent
Educational consultant: Martin Malcolm
Illustrated by Rob Davis/www.the-art-agency.co.uk
and Tom Connell/www.the-art-agency.co.uk

ISBN 978-1-4723-6037-3

Printed in China

Parents' page

The Gold Stars Key Stage 2 series

The Gold Stars Key Stage 2 series has been created to help your child revise and practise key skills and information learned in school. Each book is a complete companion to the Key Stage 2 curriculum and has been written by an expert team of teachers. The books will help to prepare your child for the SATs in year 6 and other tests that children take in school.

The books also support Scottish National Guidelines 5-14.

How to use this workbook

- Talk through the introductions to each topic and review the examples together.

- Encourage your child to tackle the fill-in activities independently.

- Keep work times short. Skip a page if it seems too difficult and return to it later.

- It doesn't matter if your child does some of the pages out of order.

- Answers to questions don't need to be complete sentences.

- Check the answers on pages 60-63. Encourage effort and reward achievement with praise.

- If your child finds any of the pages too difficult, don't worry. Children learn at different rates.

Contents

Numbers

4

Shapes

Measure

Place value

Learning objective: to learn how 3-digit numbers are made

3-digit numbers are made from hundreds,
tens and units.

Look at this number and how it is made:

593
five hundred and ninety-three

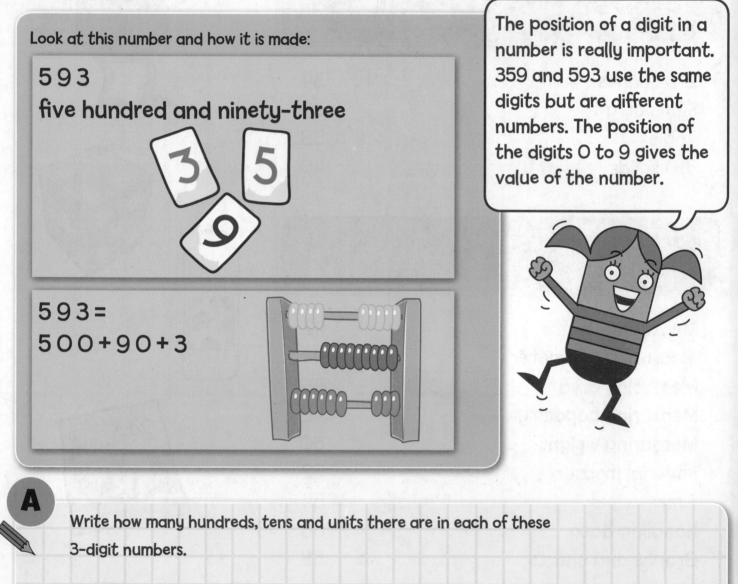

593 =
500 + 90 + 3

The position of a digit in a number is really important. 359 and 593 use the same digits but are different numbers. The position of the digits 0 to 9 gives the value of the number.

A

Write how many hundreds, tens and units there are in each of these 3-digit numbers.

1. 398 = _____ + _____ + _____

2. 217 = _____ + _____ + _____

3. 452 = _____ + _____ + _____

4. 683 = _____ + _____ + _____

5. 165 = _____ + _____ + _____

6. 709 = _____ + _____ + _____

B

Write the missing numbers or words to complete each of these.

1. 941 → nine hundred and _____

2. _____ → three hundred and twenty-six

3. 534 → _____

4. 870 → _____

5. _____ → two hundred and nineteen

6. _____ → six hundred and fifty

C

Write the numbers shown on each abacus. The first one is done for you.

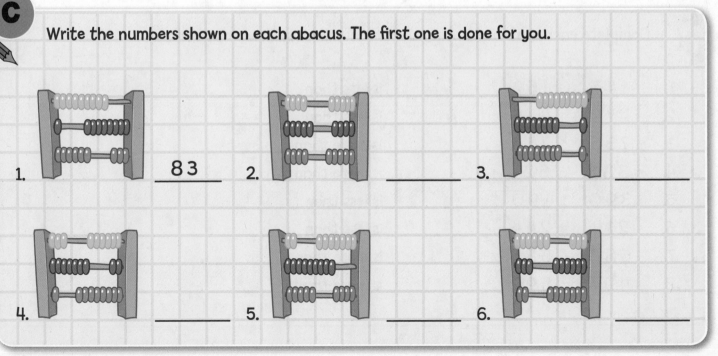

1. 83   2. _____   3. _____

4. _____   5. _____   6. _____

Ordering numbers

Learning objective: to compare 3-digit numbers and put them in order

> is the sign for 'is more than'.
< is the sign for 'is less than'.
= is the sign for 'is equal to'.

198 > 168
198 is more than 168.

126 < 211
126 is less than 211.

Look at the shape of the sign. The number next to the arrow point is smaller than the number on the other side.

You have to compare each digit in numbers to order them.

A Complete each sentence writing the two numbers in the correct place.

1.	147	152	_____ is less than _____ .
2.	479	476	_____ is less than _____ .
3.	735	753	_____ is more than _____ .
4.	381	521	_____ is more than _____ .
5.	390	190	_____ is less than _____ .
6.	214	244	_____ is less than _____ .
7.	586	585	_____ is more than _____ .
8.	497	592	_____ is more than _____ .

DEFINITION

ordering numbers: Placing numbers in order from the greatest to the smallest, or the smallest to the greatest.

B

Write in the missing $<$ or $>$ signs for each pair of numbers.

1. 264 _____ 254

4. 536 _____ 523

2. 328 _____ 431

5. 708 _____ 807

3. 190 _____ 119

6. 655 _____ 635

C

Write each group of numbers in order starting with the smallest.

1. 159   191   112   125   _____ _____ _____ _____

2. 373   387   278   483   _____ _____ _____ _____

3. 645   668   622   739   _____ _____ _____ _____

4. 461   416   460   410   _____ _____ _____ _____

5. 743   778   760   704   _____ _____ _____ _____

6. 815   309   459   195   _____ _____ _____ _____

Number sequences

Learning objective: to continue number sequences by counting on or back in steps

A number sequence is a list of numbers in a pattern. To find the rule or pattern in a sequence try finding the difference between each number.

45 → 56 → 67 → 78 → 89
+11   +11   +11   +11

The rule or pattern is +11.

990 → 980 → 970 → 960 → 950
-10   -10   -10   -10

The rule or pattern is -10.

Follow the rule to continue the sequence.

A Write the next two numbers in each sequence.

1. 22   27   32   37   ____   ____
2. 85   87   89   91   ____   ____
3. 55   52   49   46   ____   ____
4. 44   48   52   56   ____   ____
5. 100   96   92   88   ____   ____
6. 519   509   499   489   ____   ____
7. 268   368   468   568   ____   ____
8. 931   831   731   631   ____   ____

If you find these activities easy peasy, stretch your brain with the next tricky challenges!

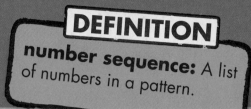

B

Write the missing numbers and the rule for each pattern.

1.	70	____	100	115	130	____	The rule is : _____
2.	650	600	550	____	____	400	The rule is : _____
3.	____	843	____	643	543	443	The rule is : _____
4.	719	____	519	____	319	219	The rule is : _____
5.	____	825	830	835	____	845	The rule is : _____
6.	462	____	482	492	____	512	The rule is : _____
7.	133	123	____	____	93	83	The rule is : _____
8.	____	515	518	521	524	____	The rule is : _____

C

Two numbers in each sequence have been swapped over. Write each correct sequence.

1. 975   985   995   965   955   945   935

____   ____   ____   ____   ____   ____   ____

2. 80   180   280   380   680   580   480

____   ____   ____   ____   ____   ____   ____

3. 853   855   857   851   849   847   845

____   ____   ____   ____   ____   ____   ____

Number trios

Learning objective: to know addition and subtraction facts

If you know an addition fact, you can work out a related subtraction fact.

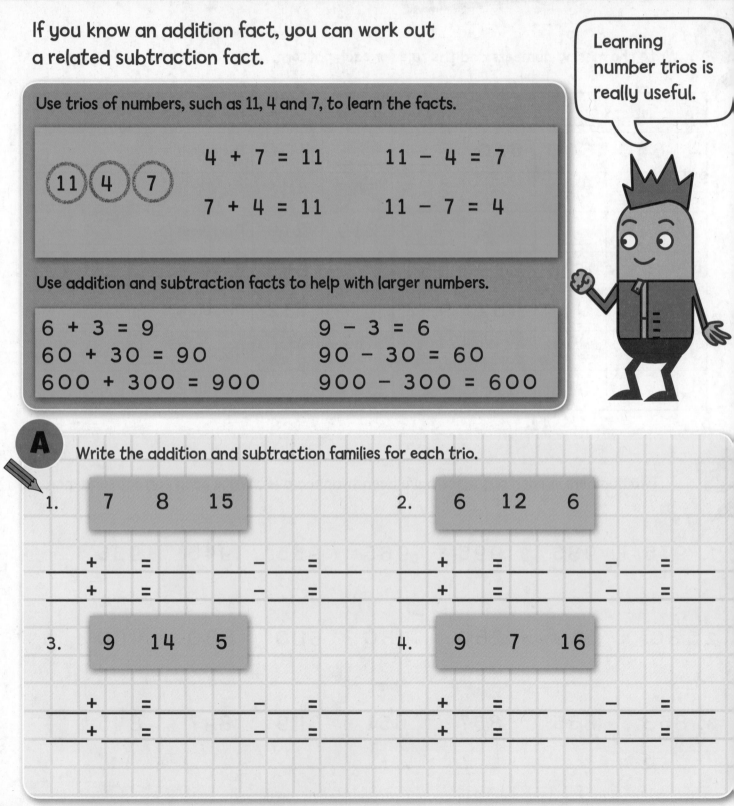

Use trios of numbers, such as 11, 4 and 7, to learn the facts.

⑪ ④ ⑦

$4 + 7 = 11$ $11 - 4 = 7$

$7 + 4 = 11$ $11 - 7 = 4$

Use addition and subtraction facts to help with larger numbers.

$6 + 3 = 9$ $9 - 3 = 6$
$60 + 30 = 90$ $90 - 30 = 60$
$600 + 300 = 900$ $900 - 300 = 600$

Learning number trios is really useful.

A

Write the addition and subtraction families for each trio.

1. | 7   8   15 |

___ + ___ = ___   ___ − ___ = ___
___ + ___ = ___   ___ − ___ = ___

2. | 6   12   6 |

___ + ___ = ___   ___ − ___ = ___
___ + ___ = ___   ___ − ___ = ___

3. | 9   14   5 |

___ + ___ = ___   ___ − ___ = ___
___ + ___ = ___   ___ − ___ = ___

4. | 9   7   16 |

___ + ___ = ___   ___ − ___ = ___
___ + ___ = ___   ___ − ___ = ___

B

Answer these.

1. 6 + 9 = _____

60 + 90 = _____

600 + 900 = _____

3. 7 + 5 = _____

70 + 50 = _____

700 + 500 = _____

2. 8 - 4 = _____

80 - 40 = _____

800 - 400 = _____

4. 9 - 7 = _____

90 - 70 = _____

900 - 700 = _____

C

Write the missing numbers.

1. 6 + ☐ = 15

2. 13 − ☐ = 5

3. ☐ − 9 = 9

4. ☐ + 8 = 12

5. 40 + ☐ = 100

6. ☐ − 200 = 700

7. 80 − ☐ = 30

8. ☐ + 400 = 600

D

Work these out in your head.

1. What is the sum of 50 and 40?

_____

4. Which number is 300 less than 900?

_____

2. What is the total of 6 and 8?

_____

5. What is 200 more than 500?

_____

3. What is the difference between 14 and 7?

_____

6. What is 80 subtract 40?

_____

Mental addition

Learning objective: to mentally add 1- and 2-digit numbers

Break numbers up so that you can add them in your head.

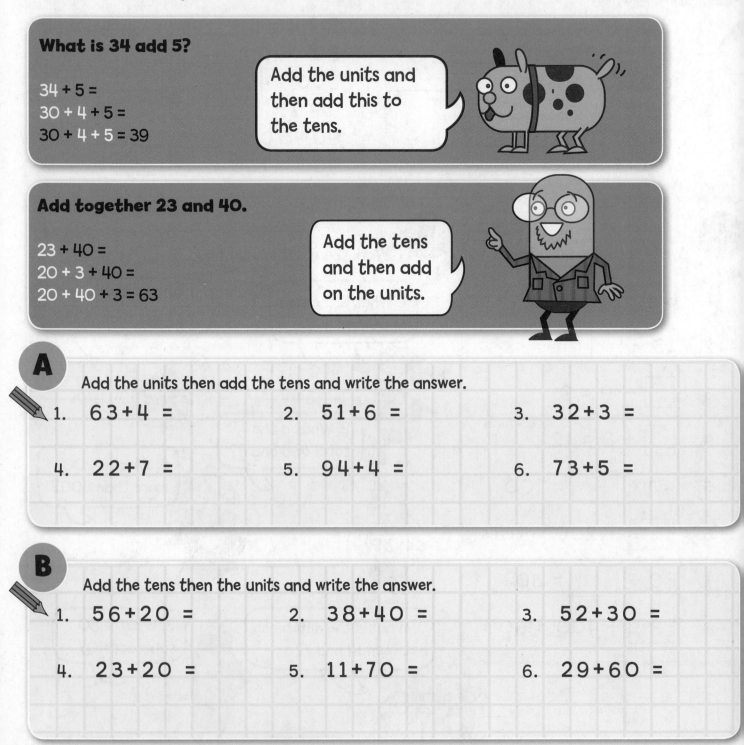

What is 34 add 5?

34 + 5 =
30 + 4 + 5 =
30 + 4 + 5 = 39

Add the units and then add this to the tens.

Add together 23 and 40.

23 + 40 =
20 + 3 + 40 =
20 + 40 + 3 = 63

Add the tens and then add on the units.

A

Add the units then add the tens and write the answer.

1. 63 + 4 =
2. 51 + 6 =
3. 32 + 3 =

4. 22 + 7 =
5. 94 + 4 =
6. 73 + 5 =

B

Add the tens then the units and write the answer.

1. 56 + 20 =
2. 38 + 40 =
3. 52 + 30 =

4. 23 + 20 =
5. 11 + 70 =
6. 29 + 60 =

C

Join the pairs of sums with the same total.

55 + 20 = ☐   29 + 50 = ☐

62 + 6 = ☐   72 + 3 = ☐

71 + 8 = ☐   48 + 20 = ☐

37 + 30 = ☐   39 + 40 = ☐

74 + 5 = ☐   63 + 4 = ☐

D

Read the first statement then work out the questions in your head.

My mother is 34.

1. My aunt is 3 years older than my mother. How old is my aunt?

_____

2. My father is 5 years older than my aunt. How old is my father?

_____

3. My grandmother was 20 when my mother was born. How old is my grandmother?

_____

4. My grandfather is 30 years older than my mother. How old is my grandfather?

_____

5. My uncle is 4 years older than my father. How old is my uncle?

_____

6. My great-grandmother is 50 years older than my mother. How old is my great-grandmother?

_____

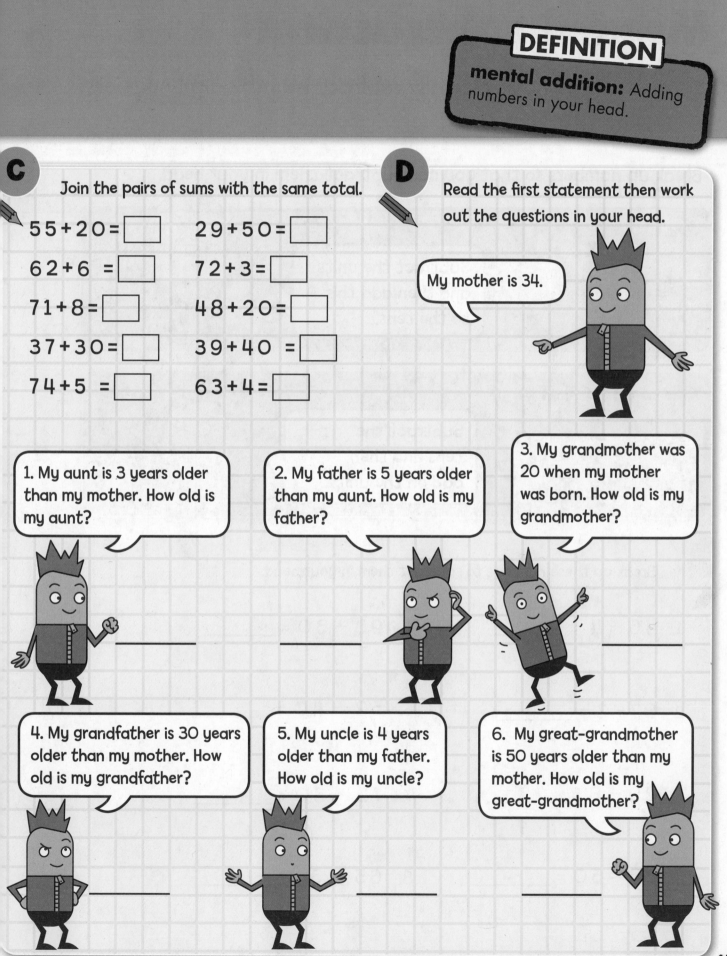

15

Mental subtraction

Learning objective: to mentally subtract 1- and 2-digit numbers

Break up numbers so that you can subtract them in your head.

What is 37 subtract 5?

37 − 5 =

30 + 7 − 5 =

30 + 7 − 5 = 32

Subtract the units and then add this to the tens.

Take away 30 from 54.

54 − 30 =

50 + 4 − 30 =

50 − 30 = 20 + 4 = 24

Subtract the tens and then add on the units.

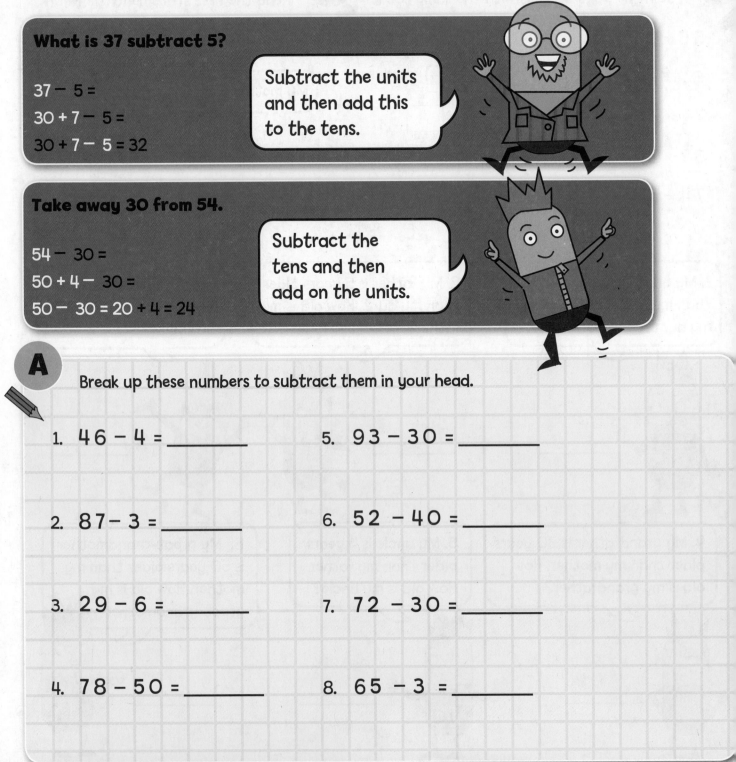

A

Break up these numbers to subtract them in your head.

1. 46 − 4 = _____

2. 87 − 3 = _____

3. 29 − 6 = _____

4. 78 − 50 = _____

5. 93 − 30 = _____

6. 52 − 40 = _____

7. 72 − 30 = _____

8. 65 − 3 = _____

DEFINITION

find the difference: Another way of saying 'subtract' or 'take away'.

B

Find the difference between each pair of numbers.

1. 98   3   _____

2. 5   57   _____

3. 3   76   _____

4. 82   40   _____

5. 20   44   _____

6. 50   91   _____

C

Complete each chart to show the numbers coming out of each subtraction machine.

1. IN   -4   OUT

IN	56	78	27	49	15	64
OUT	52					

2. IN   -30   OUT

IN	65	91	42	77	59	83
OUT	35					

17

Multiplication facts

Learning objective: to know the multiplication facts up to 10 x 10

Use the multiplication facts you already know to help learn other facts.

Example

3 x 5 = 15

3 x 6 is 3 more → 18

8 x 2 = 16

8 x 4 is double 16 → 32

10 x 6 = 60

9 x 6 is 6 less → 54

Remember 3 x 7 gives the same answer as 7 x 3.

It's easy when you know the facts!

A Answer these.

1. 6 x 4 = _____

2. 3 x 7 = _____

3. 9 x 3 = _____

6. 7 x 8 = _____

4. 5 x 9 = _____

5. 6 x 5 = _____

DEFINITION

multiplication fact: It is true that 3 x 5 = 15. This is a multiplication fact.

B Write the answers for each of these.

1. 5 x 7 = _____
   6 x 7 = _____

2. 5 x 8 = _____
   6 x 8 = _____

3. 10 x 6 = _____
   9 x 6 = _____

4. 10 x 8 = _____
   9 x 8 = _____

5. 3 x 3 = _____
   6 x 3 = _____

6. 2 x 7 = _____
   4 x 7 = _____

7. 4 x 4 = _____
   8 x 4 = _____

8. 2 x 9 = _____
   4 x 9 = _____

C Read and answer these.

1. Julie buys 4 packs of plates. What is the total number of plates she will have? _____

2. Sam buys 3 packs of straws. How many straws does he have in total? _____

3. Owen wants 12 glasses. How many packs of glasses will he need to buy? _____

4. Owen also wants 12 plates. How many packs of plates will he need to buy? _____

5. Sabina wants 20 glasses. How many packs of glasses will she need to buy? _____

6. Tess wants 20 straws. How many packs of straws does she need to buy? _____

Now see if you can complete this tricky challenge!

D

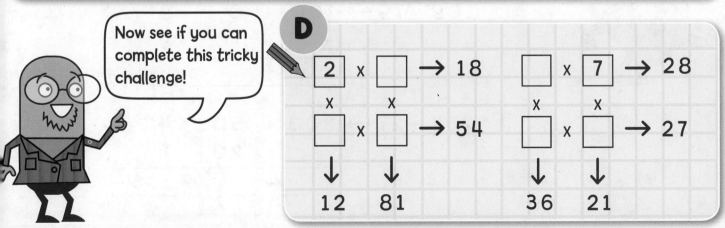

19

Written addition

When you can't work out an addition in your head, try a written method.

Example 1

$46 + 25 \rightarrow 40 + 6 + 20 + 5 = 60 + 11 = 71$

Example 2

$138 + 54$

With this short method, add the units, tens and then the hundreds.

$100 + 30 + 8$
$+ \quad\quad 50 + 4$
$\overline{100 + 80 + 12} \rightarrow 100 + 80 + 12 = 192$

$$\begin{array}{r} 138 \\ + \;\; 54 \\ \hline 192 \\ \hline 1 \end{array}$$

Make sure you line up the digits correctly.

A Add these and write the answers.

1. $267 + 18 \rightarrow$

200	+	60	+ 7
+		10	+ 8
+		+	=

2. $109 + 79 \rightarrow$

100	+	0	+ 9
+		70	+ 9
+		+	=

3. $254 + 27 \rightarrow$

200	+	50	+ 4
+		20	+ 7
+		+	=

B

Now write the answers to these.

1.	143 + 37	2.	215 + 29	3.	238 + 58	4.	126 + 35

C

Read and answer these. Use paper for your working out.

1. What is 15 more than 78? _____   4. Increase 124 by 47. _____

2. Add 57 and 26. _____   5. Total 265 and 29. _____

3. What is the total of 33 and 39? _____   6. What is 46 added to 205? _____

D

Read and answer these problems. Use paper for your working out.

1. A truck driver travels 53 kilometres in the morning and 37 kilometres in the afternoon.
   How far does the truck travel in total? _____

2. A market stall sells 28 bottles of mango juice and 39 bottles of orange juice.
   What is the total number of bottles sold? _____

3. A farmer has 44 chickens and 17 ducks.
   How many chickens and ducks are there altogether? _____

4. A postman has 149 letters and 36 parcels.
   How many items altogether are there to deliver? _____

5. Jamal has read 108 pages of his reading book and there are 52 pages left.
   How many pages in total are there in Jamal's reading book? _____

6. Julie is 136 centimetres tall and her dad is 38 centimetres taller than she is.
   How tall is Julie's dad? _____

Written subtraction

Learning objective: to subtract 2-digit numbers

When you can't work out a subtraction in your head, try a written method.

Look at these two methods.

53 - 38

Break up 53 into 40 and 13:

```
    4  13
    5  3
  - 3  8
  ──────
    1  5
```

13 - 8 = 5   40 - 30 = 10

Counting on to find the difference:

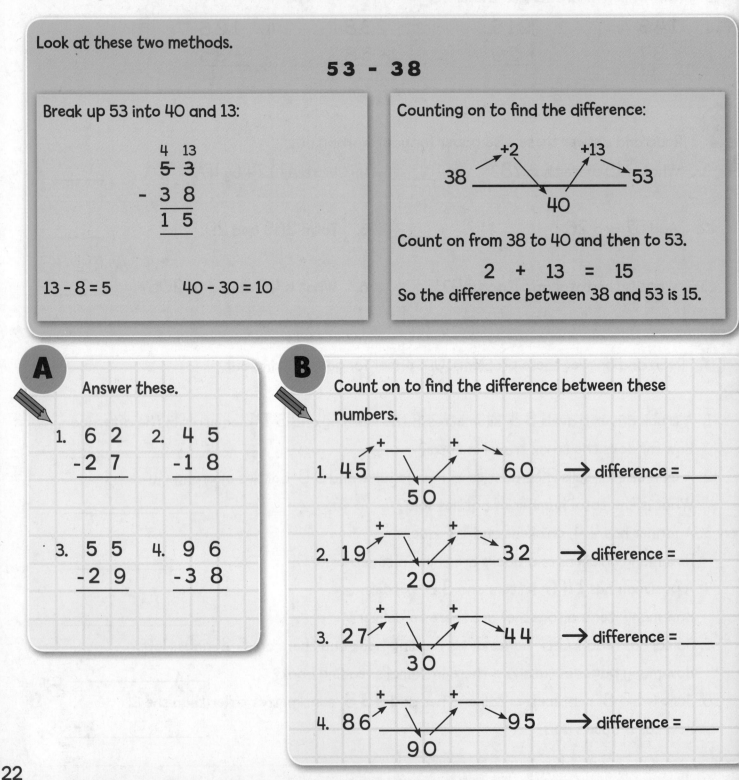

Count on from 38 to 40 and then to 53.

2 + 13 = 15

So the difference between 38 and 53 is 15.

A Answer these.

1.
```
   6 2
  -2 7
```

2.
```
   4 5
  -1 8
```

3.
```
   5 5
  -2 9
```

4.
```
   9 6
  -3 8
```

B Count on to find the difference between these numbers.

1. 45 _____ 50 _____ 60 → difference = ____

2. 19 _____ 20 _____ 32 → difference = ____

3. 27 _____ 30 _____ 44 → difference = ____

4. 86 _____ 90 _____ 95 → difference = ____

C Read and answer these.

1. What is the difference between 28 and 48? _____
2. Subtract 16 from 43. _____
3. What number is 34 less than 52? _____
4. What is 80 take away 29? _____
5. How much greater is 91 than 76? _____
6. What is 66 minus 37? _____

D

Now try this cool number puzzle!

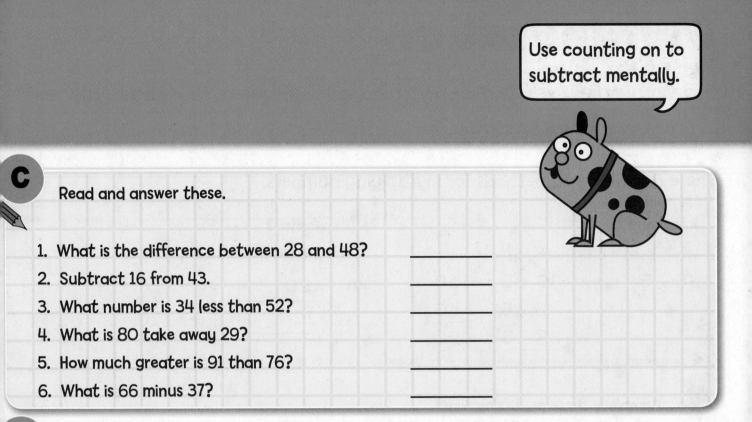

a) 2		b)	c)	
2	d)			e)
f)		g)	h)	
	i)			j)

The puzzle works like a crossword. Solve the clues and write one digit in each space. Question (a) down has been done for you.

Clues

Across	Down
a) 53 − 26	a) 44 − 22
c) 60 − 21	b) 31 − 16
d) 52 − 17	c) 59 − 23
f) 65 − 24	d) 42 − 11
h) 41 − 26	e) 60 − 15
i) 58 − 11	f) 72 − 26
j) 57 − 49	g) 64 − 27
	h) 36 − 18

23

Multiplication

Learning objective: to multiply a 2-digit number by a 1-digit number

There are different methods for multiplying numbers.

Example 1

What is 38 multiplied by 5?

38 x 5 → 30 x 5 = 150

8 x 5 = 40 +

38 x 5 = 190

Example 2

What is 24 multiplied by 6?

x	20	4
6	120	24

→ 120 + 24 = **144**

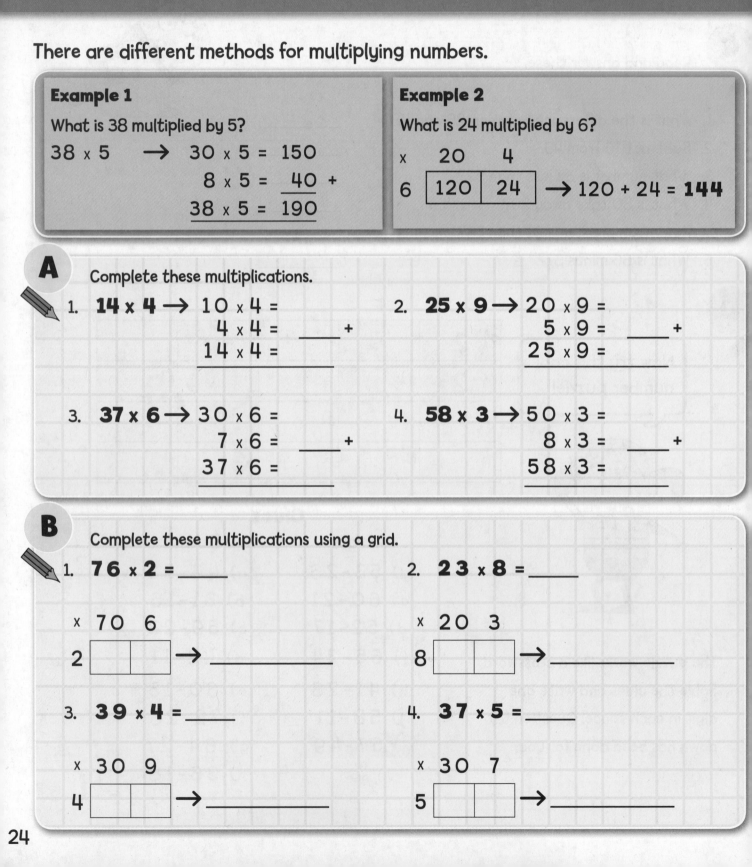

A Complete these multiplications.

1. **14 x 4** → 10 x 4 =

4 x 4 = _____ +

14 x 4 = _____

2. **25 x 9** → 20 x 9 =

5 x 9 = _____ +

25 x 9 = _____

3. **37 x 6** → 30 x 6 =

7 x 6 = _____ +

37 x 6 = _____

4. **58 x 3** → 50 x 3 =

8 x 3 = _____ +

58 x 3 = _____

B Complete these multiplications using a grid.

1. **76 x 2** = _____

x	70	6
2		

→ _____

2. **23 x 8** = _____

x	20	3
8		

→ _____

3. **39 x 4** = _____

x	30	9
4		

→ _____

4. **37 x 5** = _____

x	30	7
5		

→ _____

DEFINITION

multiplication: This is like repeated addition.

C

Answer these. Choose a method for working out each answer. Use paper for your working out.

1. 86 x 2 = _____
2. 47 x 3 = _____
3. 19 x 9 = _____
4. 23 x 8 = _____
5. 34 x 6 = _____
6. 28 x 5 = _____

D

Read and answer these problems.

1. A bus holds 48 passengers. How many people will 4 buses hold?

   _____

2. Mr Duke travels 19 kilometres each day to and from work. He works 5 days a week. How far does he travel altogether in a week?

   _____

3. A market stall has 6 crates of melons. There are 35 melons in a crate. How many melons are there in total?

   _____

4. A farmer fills 4 trays of eggs. Each tray holds 36 eggs. How many eggs does the farmer have?

   _____

5. The battery in a mobile phone lasts 7 days. How many hours does the battery last?

   _____

6. A dog eats 59 dog biscuits per day. How many will it eat in 3 days?

   _____

Break the problem down into smaller steps.

Use the multiplication facts that you know.

Division

Learning objective: to use written methods to divide

If you know your multiplication facts it can help you to divide numbers.

Look at the trio 6, 3 and 18:

$6 \times 3 = 18$ $3 \times 6 = 18$

$18 \div 3 = 6$ $18 \div 6 = 3$

If a number cannot be divided exactly it leaves a remainder.

Example

What is 35 divided by 4?

Work out how many groups of 4 are in 35 and what is left over:

$$\begin{array}{r} 8\,r\,3 \\ 4\overline{)3\,5} \\ -3\,2 \quad (4 \times 8) \\ \hline 3 \end{array}$$

← **Answer**

$35 \div 4 = 8$ remainder 3

> Division is the opposite of multiplication.

A Copy and complete these and find the remainders.

1.
$$5\overline{)4\,8}\quad r\_\_$$
$$\_\_ (5 \times 9)$$
$$\_\_$$

2.
$$6\overline{)3\,7}\quad r\_\_$$
$$\_\_ (6 \times 6)$$
$$\_\_$$

3.
$$9\overline{)6\,5}\quad r\_\_$$
$$\_\_ (9 \times 7)$$
$$\_\_$$

4.
$$3\overline{)2\,6}\quad r\_\_$$
$$\_\_ (\_ \times \_)$$
$$\_\_$$

5.
$$7\overline{)4\,0}\quad r\_\_$$
$$\_\_ (\_ \times \_)$$
$$\_\_$$

6.
$$8\overline{)5\,2}\quad r\_\_$$
$$\_\_ (\_ \times \_)$$
$$\_\_$$

B

Complete these.

1. ___ ÷ 4 = 7

2. 18 ÷ ___ = 2

3. ___ x 6 = 36

4. 40 ÷ 5 = ___

5. 8 x ___ = 24

6. ___ x 7 = 21

7. 54 ÷ ___ = 9

8. 6 x ___ = 48

9. 63 ÷ 9 = ___

10. ___ ÷ 4 = 8

I'm thinking of a number. It is less than 100 and if I divide it by 2, 3, 4, 5, 6 or 10 it leaves a remainder of 1. What is my number?

C

Mrs Folkes is grouping her class into teams. She has 35 pupils in her class.

Read and answer these questions:

1. The School Maths Quiz has 3 pupils in each team. How many quiz teams can be made from Mrs Folkes' class? _____

2. Helper Teams have 8 children to help around the school. Any children left over will join children from another class. How many children will be left over in Mrs Folkes' class? _____

3. Mrs Folkes is dividing her class into sports teams. Complete this chart.

Sport	Number of players in each team	Total number of teams	Number of students left over
Doubles Tennis	2 players per team	17 teams	1 left over
400m Relay Race	4 players per team	8 teams	
Basketball	5 players per team		0 left over
Volleyball	6 players per team		
Netball	7 players per team		

Fractions of quantities

Learning objective: to find fractions of numbers and quantities

Fractions have a numerator and a denominator.

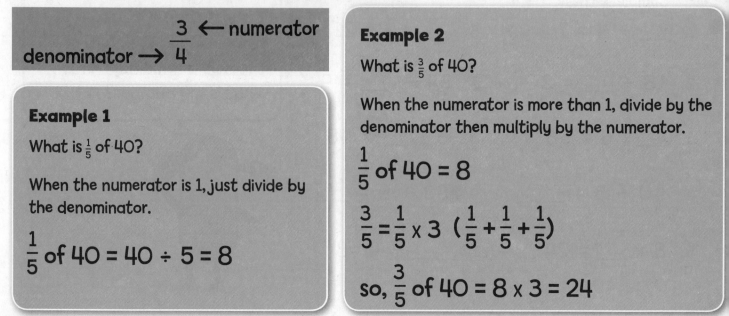

$$\frac{3}{4} \leftarrow \text{numerator}$$
denominator $\rightarrow$

Example 1

What is $\frac{1}{5}$ of 40?

When the numerator is 1, just divide by the denominator.

$\frac{1}{5}$ of $40 = 40 \div 5 = 8$

Example 2

What is $\frac{3}{5}$ of 40?

When the numerator is more than 1, divide by the denominator then multiply by the numerator.

$\frac{1}{5}$ of $40 = 8$

$\frac{3}{5} = \frac{1}{5} \times 3 \ (\frac{1}{5} + \frac{1}{5} + \frac{1}{5})$

so, $\frac{3}{5}$ of $40 = 8 \times 3 = 24$

A

Use the dots to work out these fractions.

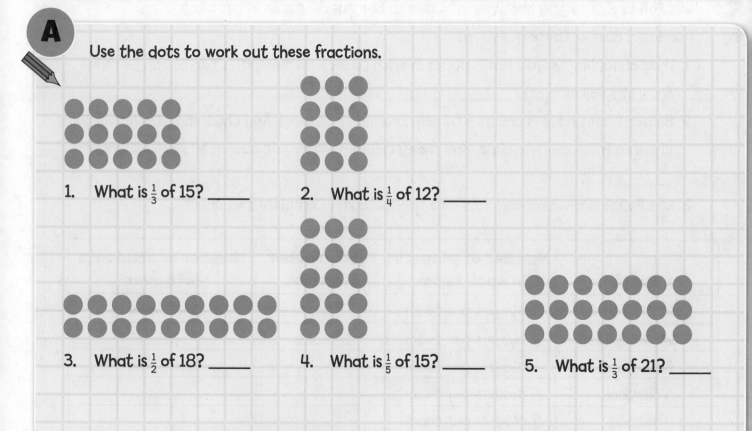

1.   What is $\frac{1}{3}$ of 15? _____

2.   What is $\frac{1}{4}$ of 12? _____

3.   What is $\frac{1}{2}$ of 18? _____

4.   What is $\frac{1}{5}$ of 15? _____

5.   What is $\frac{1}{3}$ of 21? _____

DEFINITION

fraction: This is a part of a whole.
quantity: How much of something there is.

B

There are 24 balloons of different shapes and colours in a pack. How many of each type of balloon are there?

$\frac{1}{2}$ are red: _____ red balloons

$\frac{1}{6}$ are yellow: _____ yellow balloons

$\frac{1}{3}$ are blue: _____ blue balloons

$\frac{1}{4}$ are large balloons: _____ large balloons

$\frac{1}{8}$ are long balloons: _____ long balloons

24 ASSORTED BALLOONS

David has 64 sweets. He gives $\frac{1}{2}$ to his classmates. How many does he have left?

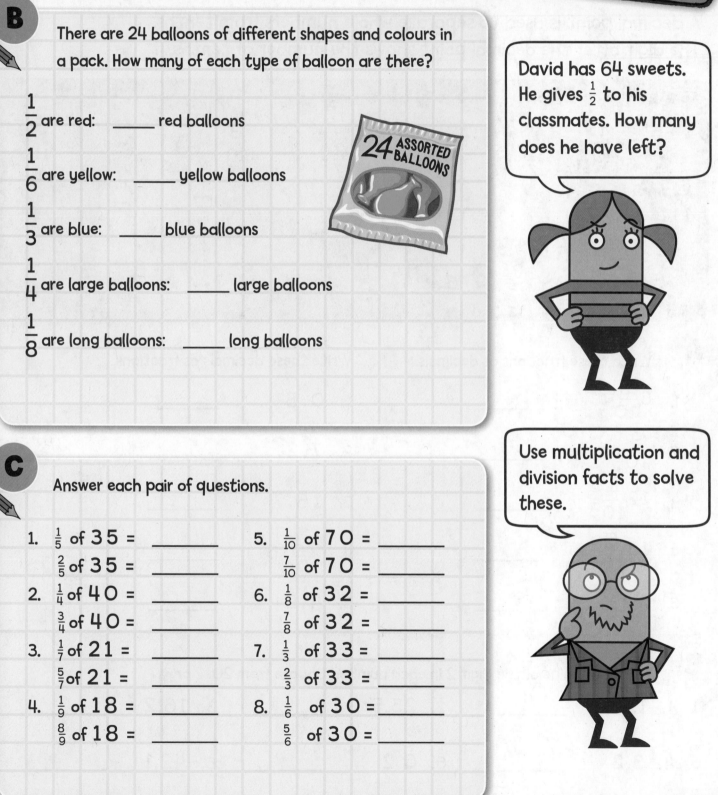

C

Answer each pair of questions.

1. $\frac{1}{5}$ of 35 = _____
   $\frac{2}{5}$ of 35 = _____

2. $\frac{1}{4}$ of 40 = _____
   $\frac{3}{4}$ of 40 = _____

3. $\frac{1}{7}$ of 21 = _____
   $\frac{5}{7}$ of 21 = _____

4. $\frac{1}{9}$ of 18 = _____
   $\frac{8}{9}$ of 18 = _____

5. $\frac{1}{10}$ of 70 = _____
   $\frac{7}{10}$ of 70 = _____

6. $\frac{1}{8}$ of 32 = _____
   $\frac{7}{8}$ of 32 = _____

7. $\frac{1}{3}$ of 33 = _____
   $\frac{2}{3}$ of 33 = _____

8. $\frac{1}{6}$ of 30 = _____
   $\frac{5}{6}$ of 30 = _____

Use multiplication and division facts to solve these.

Decimals

Learning objective: to use and understand tenths

A decimal point is used to separate whole numbers from tenths.
The digit after the decimal point shows the number of tenths.

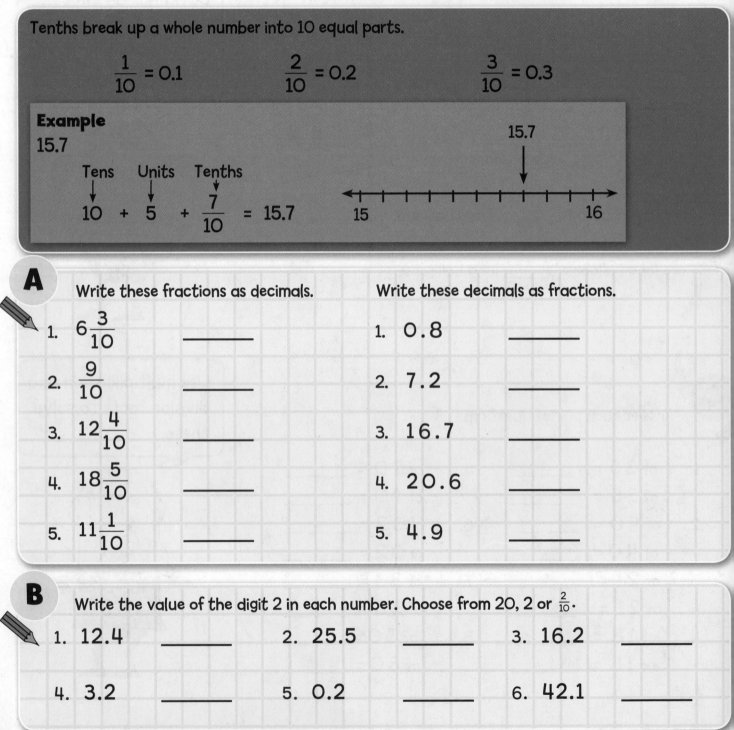

Tenths break up a whole number into 10 equal parts.

$$\frac{1}{10} = 0.1 \qquad \frac{2}{10} = 0.2 \qquad \frac{3}{10} = 0.3$$

Example
15.7

Tens   Units   Tenths

$$10 \ + \ 5 \ + \ \frac{7}{10} \ = \ 15.7$$

15.7

15   16

A Write these fractions as decimals.

1. $6\frac{3}{10}$ _____

2. $\frac{9}{10}$ _____

3. $12\frac{4}{10}$ _____

4. $18\frac{5}{10}$ _____

5. $11\frac{1}{10}$ _____

Write these decimals as fractions.

1. 0.8 _____

2. 7.2 _____

3. 16.7 _____

4. 20.6 _____

5. 4.9 _____

B Write the value of the digit 2 in each number. Choose from 20, 2 or $\frac{2}{10}$.

1. 12.4 _____

2. 25.5 _____

3. 16.2 _____

4. 3.2 _____

5. 0.2 _____

6. 42.1 _____

DEFINITION

decimal point: A point that separates whole numbers from tenths.

C

Look at these number lines and write the decimal number above each arrow.

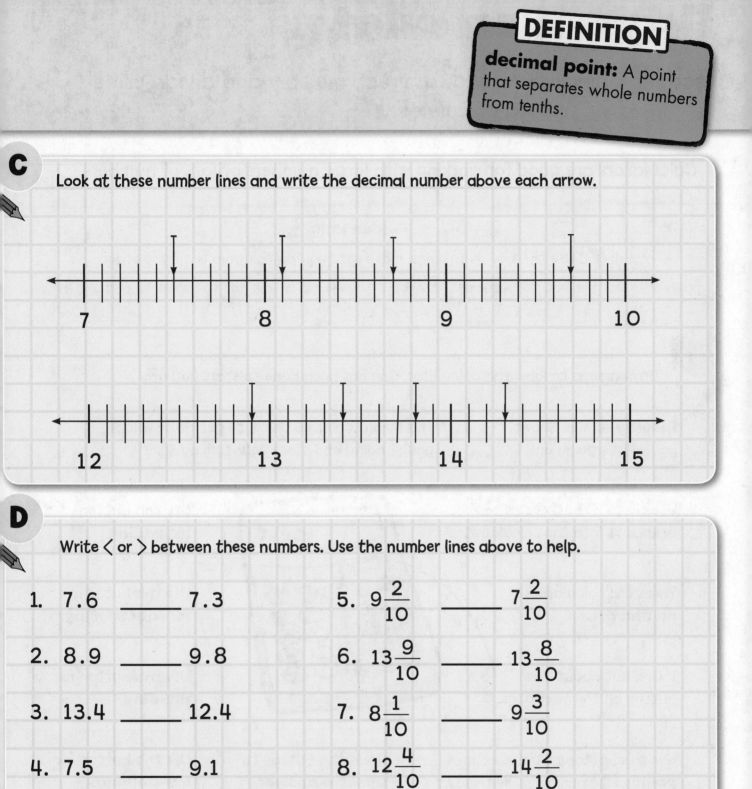

7   8   9   10

12   13   14   15

D

Write $<$ or $>$ between these numbers. Use the number lines above to help.

1. 7.6 _____ 7.3

2. 8.9 _____ 9.8

3. 13.4 _____ 12.4

4. 7.5 _____ 9.1

5. $9\frac{2}{10}$ _____ $7\frac{2}{10}$

6. $13\frac{9}{10}$ _____ $13\frac{8}{10}$

7. $8\frac{1}{10}$ _____ $9\frac{3}{10}$

8. $12\frac{4}{10}$ _____ $14\frac{2}{10}$

Look back at page 8 to find out what $<$ and $>$ mean.

Using a calculator

Calculators are good for working with large numbers or lots of numbers.

Golden Rule

If you use the **x** or **÷** buttons, make sure you do things in the right order.

6 + 2 **x** 5 is not the same as 2 **x** 5 + 6   4 + 6 ÷ 2 is not the same as 6 ÷ 2 + 4

A

Draw arrows to label this calculator. One has been done to start you off.

Display screen. Shows you what's going on.

This means **cancel**. Use it to get rid of what you're doing and start your sum again.

Use these 10 buttons to tap **numbers** into the calculator.

Use this button for **adding**.

Turns the calculator **on and off**.

Use this button for **subtracting**.

√ Find out about this button on the next page.

Use this button for **dividing**.

Use this button to put **decimal points** into numbers, like this: 0.5

Press this button to show the **answer**.

Use this button for **multiplying**.

1. What's the **biggest** figure you can tap in? Write it here:

_____

2. What's the **smallest** figure you can tap in, using a decimal point?

_____

B

Follow these **calculator trails**. Tap the instructions into your calculator and write your answer in the diamond. Can you see a pattern in the diamonds?

| 5 | ×12 | -10 | ÷2 | +75 | -99 | +4= | ◆ |

| 4 | +96 | ÷4 | -5 | ×3 | -51 | +1= | ◆ |

| 284 | ×8 | -72 | ÷400 | -0.5 | +12 | -2= | ◆ |

Make your own calculator trail. It must end with the answer in the diamond.

| | = | 20 |

C

What is this button for? √ Follow these instructions to find out. Remember to press **cancel** after each answer.

> Try tapping some numbers into your calculator!

1. Tap number **9** into the calculator. Press √. You get the answer ___
2. Tap number **25** into the calculator. Press √. You get the answer ___
3. Tap number **4** into the calculator. Press √. You get the answer ___
4. Tap number **36** into the calculator. Press √. You get the answer ___
5. Tap number **81** into the calculator. Press √. You get the answer ___

Tick the box that explains what the button does.

| It always divides your starting number by 3, 5 or 2. ☐ | It always finds what number multiplied by itself makes your starting number. ☐ | It always subtracts exactly one third of your starting number. ☐ |

33

2-D shapes

Learning objective: to name, draw and describe 2-D shapes

2-D shapes are flat shapes. They can have straight or curved sides.

These are the names of some polygons (a 2-D shape with straight sides).

| Triangle 3 sides | Quadrilateral 4 sides | Pentagon 5 sides |
| Hexagon 6 sides | Heptagon 7 sides | Octagon 8 sides |

A

Write the name for each shape. Count the number of sides to help find the shape name.

1. _____

2. _____

3. _____

4. _____

5. _____

6. _____

B

Write the name of the shapes in each set and the odd one out.

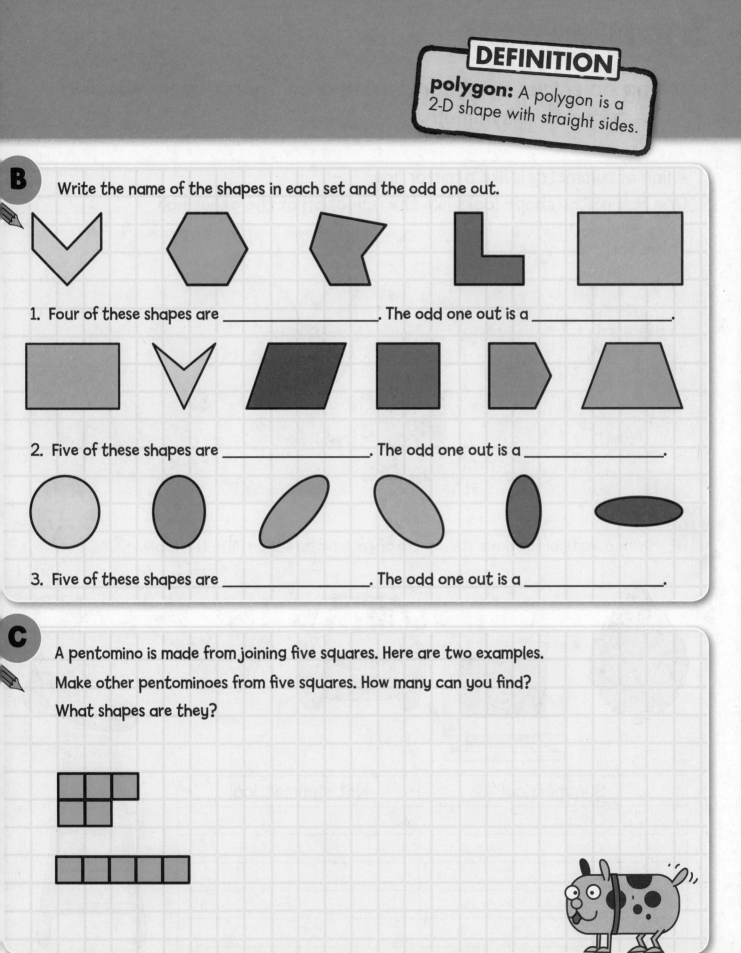

1. Four of these shapes are _____. The odd one out is a _____.

2. Five of these shapes are _____. The odd one out is a _____.

3. Five of these shapes are _____. The odd one out is a _____.

C

A pentomino is made from joining five squares. Here are two examples.

Make other pentominoes from five squares. How many can you find?

What shapes are they?

Symmetry

Learning objective: to recognize and draw shapes with reflective symmetry

A line of symmetry is like a mirror line.

One half of the shape looks like the reflection of the other half.

Look at these lines of symmetry.

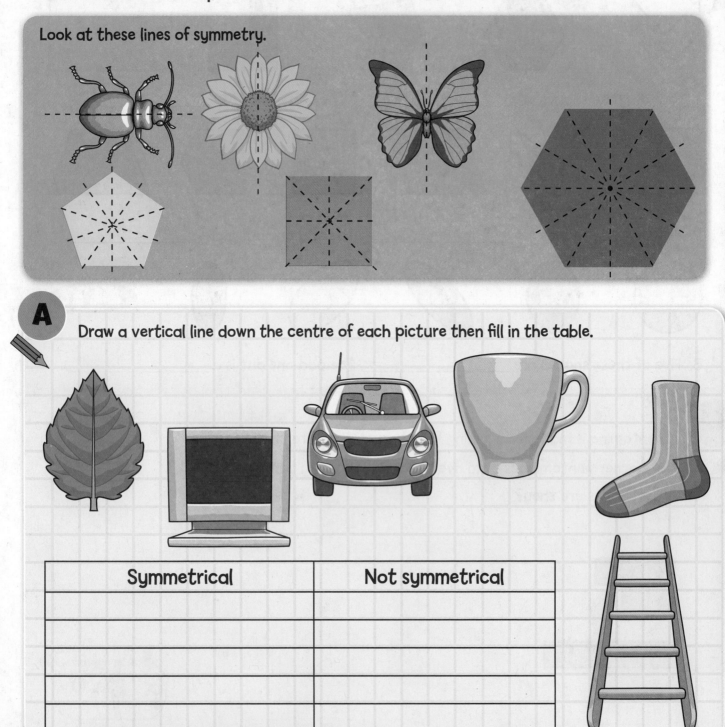

A

Draw a vertical line down the centre of each picture then fill in the table.

Symmetrical	Not symmetrical

symmetry: When one half of a shape looks like an exact reflection of the other half.

B

Complete these drawings to make symmetrical shapes.

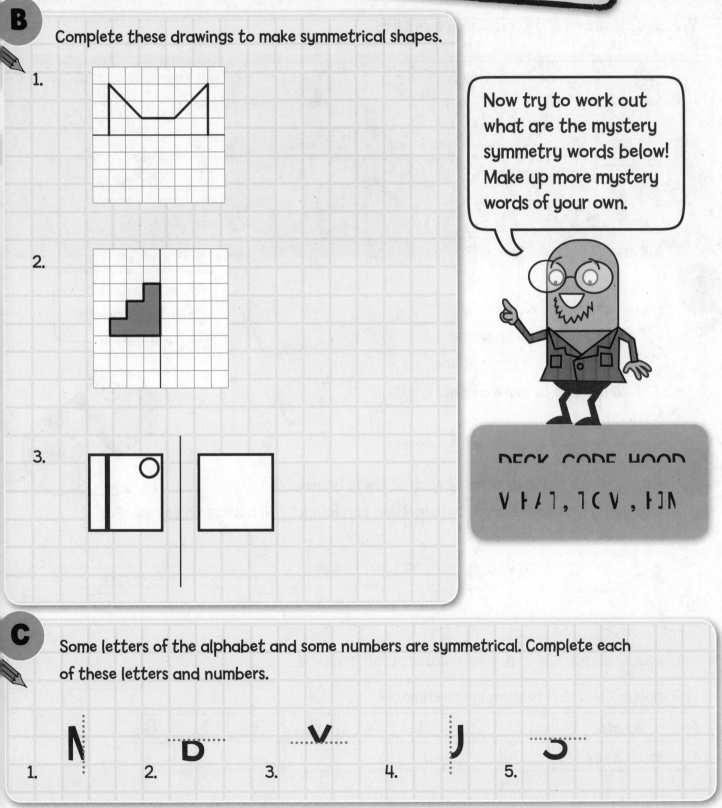

1.

2.

3.

Now try to work out what are the mystery symmetry words below! Make up more mystery words of your own.

DECK CODE HOOD

V ƃ/7, 7C V , ƃꓵ

C

Some letters of the alphabet and some numbers are symmetrical. Complete each of these letters and numbers.

N
1.

D
2.

V
3.

J
4.

ꓛ
5.

Angles

Learning objective: to use degrees to measure angles

We use degrees (°) to measure angles.

A ¼ turn is also called a right angle.
There are 90 degrees (90°) in a right angle.

A complete turn is the same as four right angles, or 360°.

A straight line is the same as two right angles, or 180°.

A

1. Take a piece of scrap paper.
2. Fold it to make a straight line.
3. Fold it again to make a right angle.

An estimate is your best guess.

B

Estimate the size in degrees of each of these angles.

Use your folded right angle to help. (You can fold 90° in half again to make 45°.)

1.   2.   3.   4.

5.   6.   7.   8.

Complete the table to show your estimates.

Angle	1.	2.	3.	4.	5.	6.	7.	8.
Estimated size (°)								

DEFINITION

angle: The amount by which something turns is an angle.

C

Draw the right angles on these shapes. The first one has been done for you.

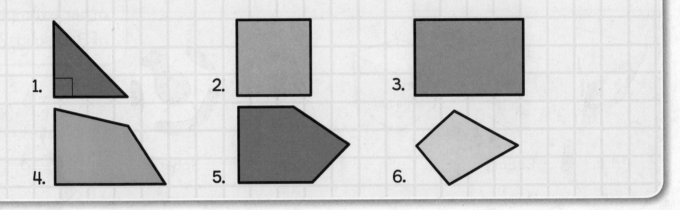

1.   2.   3.

4.   5.   6.

D

Look at these 6 angles. Estimate the size of each angle.

Now write them in order of size, starting with the smallest: ___ ___ ___ ___ ___ ___

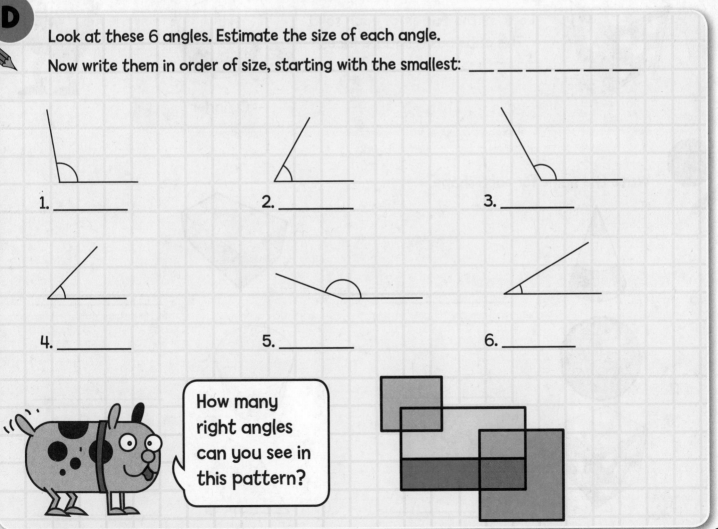

1. _____   2. _____   3. _____

4. _____   5. _____   6. _____

How many right angles can you see in this pattern?

3-D solids

Learning objective: to name and describe 3-D solids

There are 3-D solids all around you.

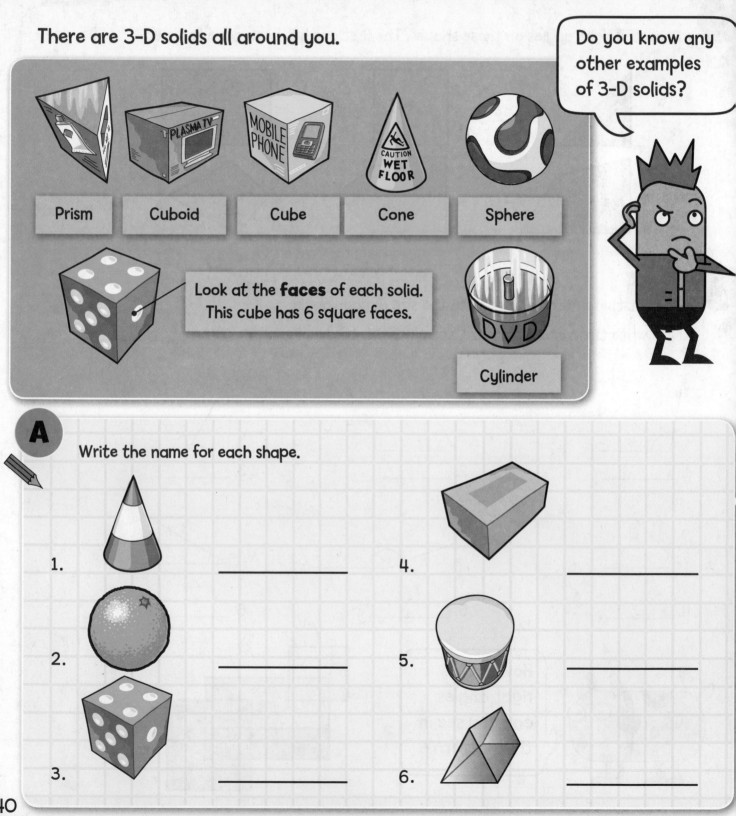

Prism   Cuboid   Cube   Cone   Sphere

Look at the **faces** of each solid. This cube has 6 square faces.

Cylinder

Do you know any other examples of 3-D solids?

A Write the name for each shape.

1. _____

2. _____

3. _____

4. _____

5. _____

6. _____

DEFINITION

face: The flat surface of a solid shape is called a face.

B

Name the shapes in each set and find the odd one out.

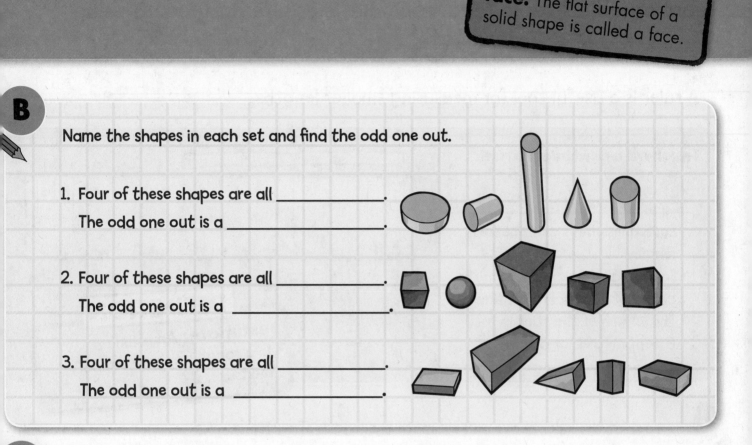

1. Four of these shapes are all _____.

   The odd one out is a _____.

2. Four of these shapes are all _____.

   The odd one out is a _____.

3. Four of these shapes are all _____.

   The odd one out is a _____.

C

Complete this chart.

Name of shape	cube	cuboid	prism
Total number of faces			
Number of square and rectangle faces			
Number of triangular faces			

D

Are these statements **always**, **sometimes** or **never** true?

1. A cuboid has a triangular face. _____

2. A cone has a circular face. _____

3. A cylinder has two circular faces of different sizes. _____

4. A prism has a square face.

   _____

41

Measuring length

A ruler is a useful tool for measuring smaller lengths.

This shows a **centimetre** ruler.

• Each division is 1 centimetre in length.
• Each small division between the centimetres is half a centimetre.
• The length of the stick is 6 centimetres, or 6cm.

DEFINITION

estimate: An estimate is a rough answer, without measuring.

A

Look at the ruler above and estimate the length of each line.

Write your estimate in centimetres.

1. estimate: _____cm
_____

2. estimate: _____cm
_____

3. estimate: _____cm
_____

4. estimate: _____cm
_____

5. estimate: _____cm
_____

6. estimate: _____cm
_____

Take your best guess!

B Use a ruler and measure the exact length of each line in Section A.

Write each length in centimetres.

1. length: _____ cm

2. length: _____ cm

3. length: _____ cm

4. length: _____ cm

5. length: _____ cm

6. length: _____ cm

C Measure each item and write the lengths.

1. cotton: _____ cm

2. needle: _____ cm

3. paperclip: _____ cm

4. zip: _____ cm

5. screwdriver: _____ cm

6. screw: _____ cm

7. nail: _____ cm

8. toothbrush: _____ cm

Measuring perimeter

Learning objective: to measure the perimeter of rectangles

The perimeter of a shape is the distance all around the edge.

This tile has a perimeter of 3cm + 3cm + 5cm + 5cm = 16cm

Use a ruler to check these measurements.

A

Calculate the distance round each of these shapes. Write the perimeters in metres.

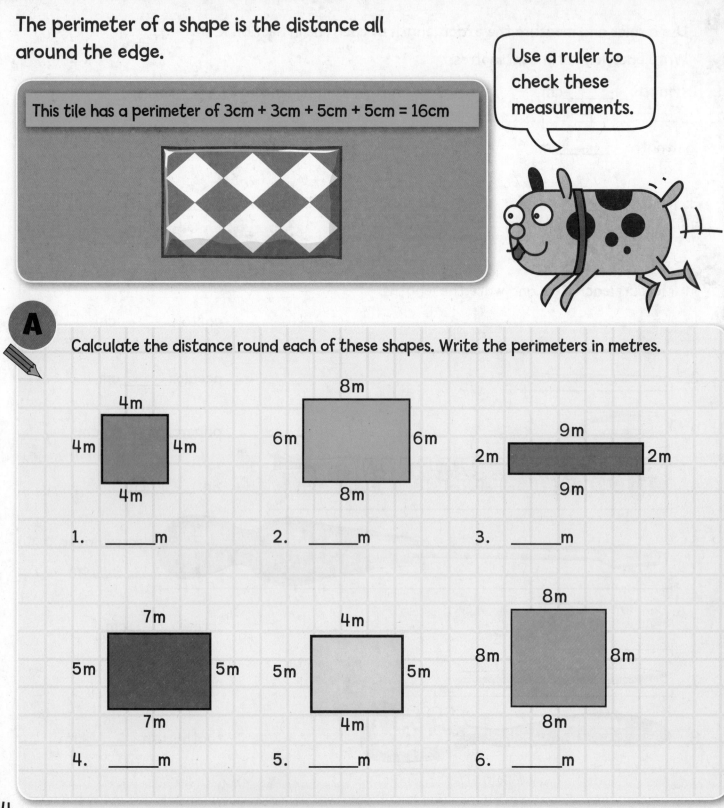

4m
4m   4m
4m

1. _____m

8m
6m   6m
8m

2. _____m

9m
2m   2m
9m

3. _____m

7m
5m   5m
7m

4. _____m

4m
5m   5m
4m

5. _____m

8m
8m   8m
8m

6. _____m

B

Use a ruler to measure the sides of each rectangle. Write the length, height and perimeter for these in centimetres.

1.
Length = _____cm

Height = _____cm

Perimeter = _____cm

2.
Length = _____cm

Height = _____cm

Perimeter = _____cm

3.
Length = _____cm

Height = _____cm

Perimeter = _____cm

4.
Length = _____cm

Height = _____cm

Perimeter = _____cm

5.
Length = _____cm

Height = _____cm

Perimeter = _____cm

6.
Length = _____cm

Height = _____cm

Perimeter = _____cm

C

Complete this chart. Write the length and height of each rectangle and calculate the perimeter.

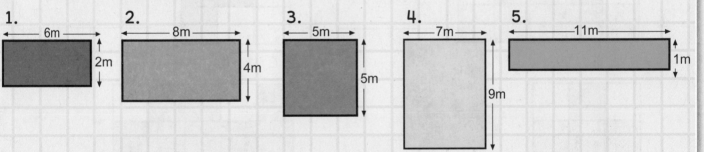

1. 6m / 2m
2. 8m / 4m
3. 5m / 5m
4. 7m / 9m
5. 11m / 1m

Rectangle	length	add	height	Multiply total by 2	Perimeter
1	m	+	m	=	m → x 2	m
2	m	+	m	=	m → x 2	m
3	m	+	m	=	m → x 2	m
4	m	+	m	=	m → x 2	m
5	m	+	m	=	m → x 2	m

Measuring area

Learning objective: to find the area of shapes on a square grid

To find the area of a shape you can draw it on a square grid and count the squares.

> The side of each small square on this grid is 1cm.

This shape has an area of 12 square centimetres.

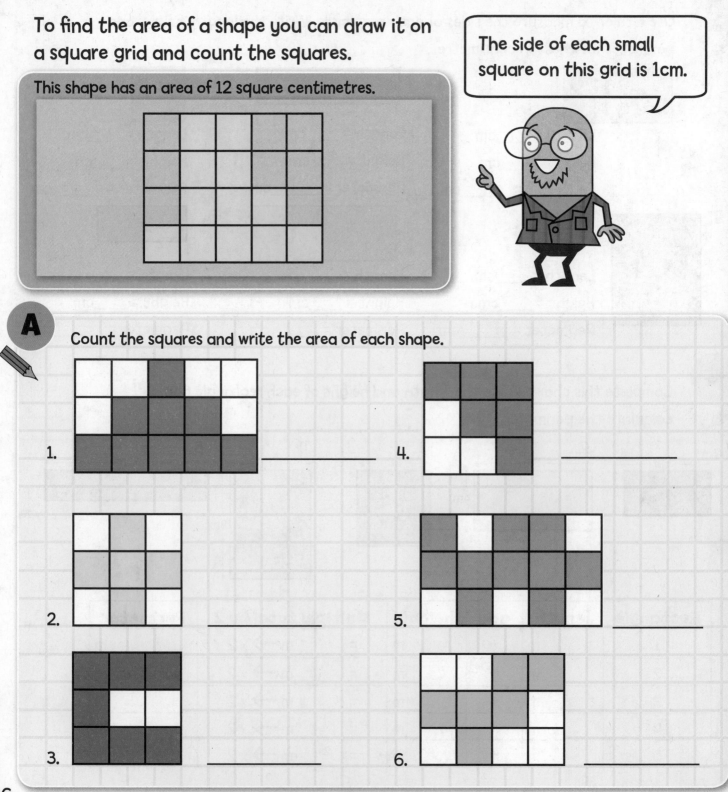

A

Count the squares and write the area of each shape.

1. _____

2. _____

3. _____

4. _____

5. _____

6. _____

46

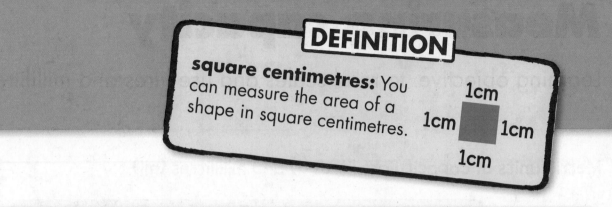

B

This plan shows the gardens of a hotel. Each square shows 1 square metre of ground. Count the squares and write the area for each section.

1. Area of swimming pool
= _____ square metres

2. Area of paths = _____ square metres

3. Area of car park = _____ square metres

4. Area of grass = _____ square metres

5. Area of flower border
= _____ square metres

C

A gardener is planning a path using 8 slabs. Each slab is 1 square metre. Here are two designs using 8 squares. Draw 3 more path designs using 8 squares.

Measuring capacity

Learning objective: to read scales and use litres and millilitres

Metric units of capacity are litres (l) and millilitres (ml).

> There are 1000ml in 1l.
>
> 1000 millilitres = 1 litre
>
> 1l — 1000ml

A

Write the amount shown in each jug. Look carefully at the units of measurement for each jug.

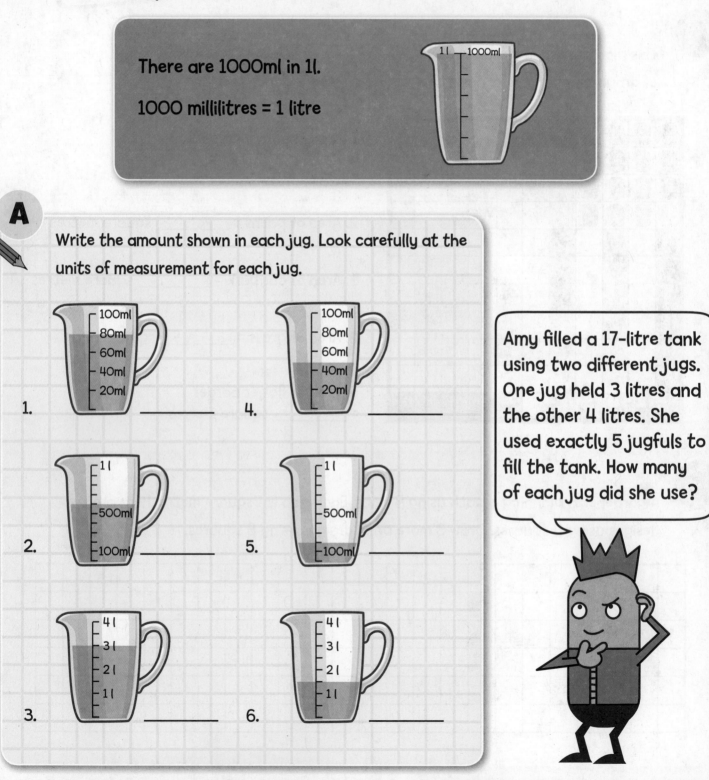

1. _____

2. _____

3. _____

4. _____

5. _____

6. _____

Amy filled a 17-litre tank using two different jugs. One jug held 3 litres and the other 4 litres. She used exactly 5 jugfuls to fill the tank. How many of each jug did she use?

B Each of these containers holds a different amount.

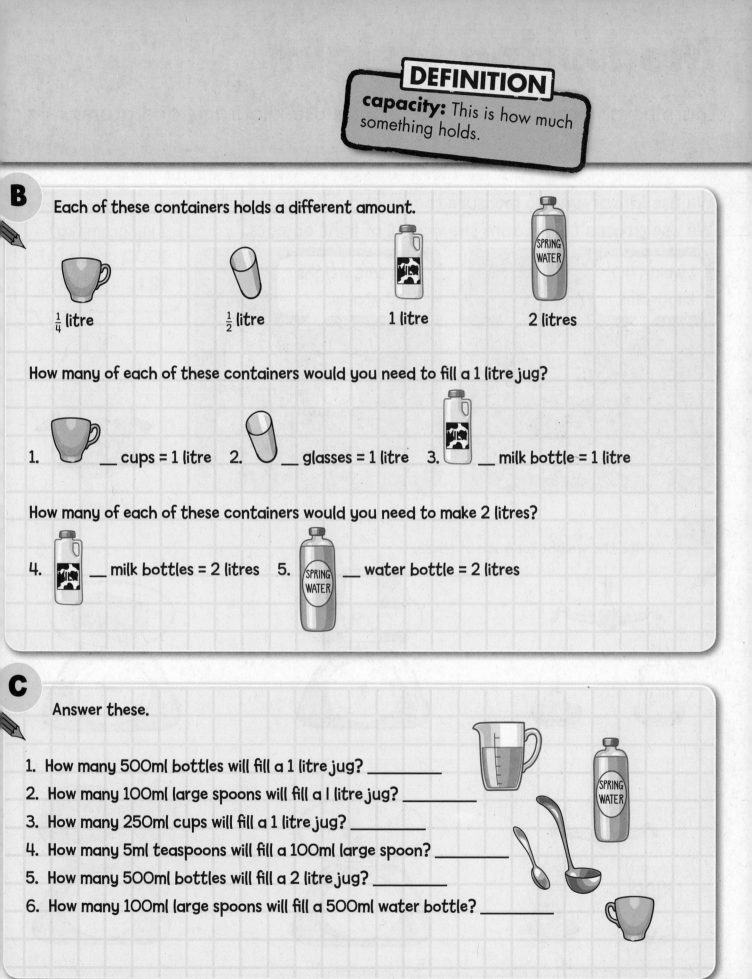

$\frac{1}{4}$ litre $\frac{1}{2}$ litre   1 litre   2 litres

How many of each of these containers would you need to fill a 1 litre jug?

1. __ cups = 1 litre   2. __ glasses = 1 litre   3. __ milk bottle = 1 litre

How many of each of these containers would you need to make 2 litres?

4. __ milk bottles = 2 litres   5. __ water bottle = 2 litres

C Answer these.

1. How many 500ml bottles will fill a 1 litre jug? _____
2. How many 100ml large spoons will fill a 1 litre jug? _____
3. How many 250ml cups will fill a 1 litre jug? _____
4. How many 5ml teaspoons will fill a 100ml large spoon? _____
5. How many 500ml bottles will fill a 2 litre jug? _____
6. How many 100ml large spoons will fill a 500ml water bottle? _____

Measuring weight

Learning objective: to read scales and use kilograms and grams

We use **kilograms** to measure the weight of heavy objects.
We use **grams** to measure the weight of light objects.

I weigh 40 kilograms.

This salt weighs 500 grams.

1 kilogram (kg) = 1000 grams (g)
12 kg = 12000g

A

Write the weight for each of these.

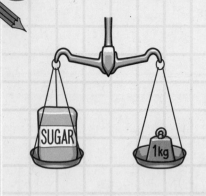

1. _____ kg

2. _____ kg

3. _____ kg

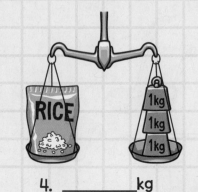

4. _____ kg

5. _____ kg

6. _____ kg

B Convert these measures.

1. 2000g = _____ kg

2. 5kg = _____ g

3. 4000g = _____ kg

4. 6kg = _____ g

5. 9kg = _____ g

6. 3000g = _____ kg

These shapes weigh 18kg altogether. If each pyramid weighs 3kg, what is the weight of each cube?

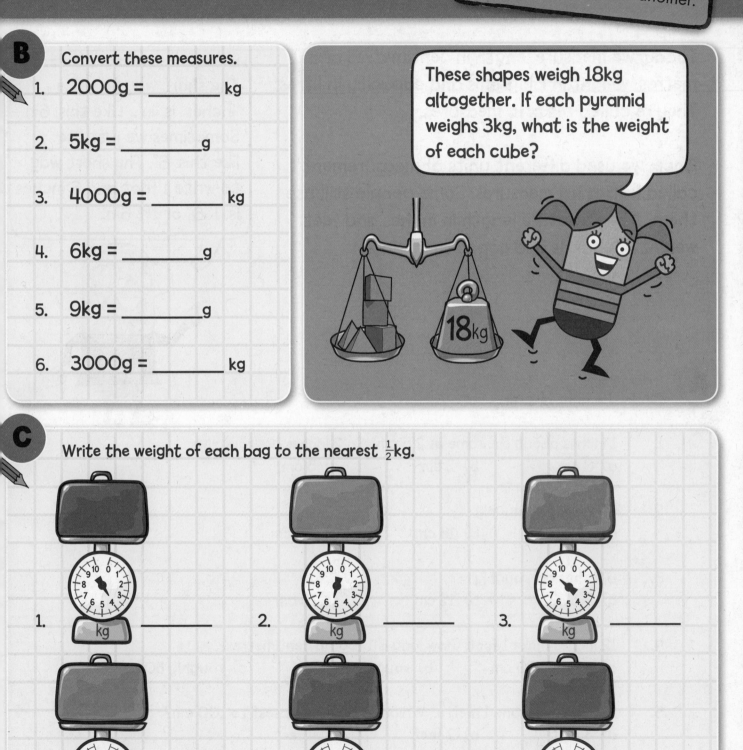

C Write the weight of each bag to the nearest ½kg.

1. kg _____

2. kg _____

3. kg _____

4. kg _____

5. kg _____

6. kg _____

Imperial measures

Learning objective: to know approximate equivalent imperial units for common metric measures

Today, we measure length in centimetres and metres, weight in kilograms and capacity in litres. They're called **metric** measures.

Once, we used different units of measurement called **imperial** measures. Some people still use them. They measure length in inches and feet, weight in pounds and capacity in pints.

The short way to write 'inches' is 'in'. Like this: 6in. Sometimes we just use ", like this: 6". The short way to write 1 foot and 6 inches is: 1' 6" or 1ft 6in.

A

Circle the right answer.

1. 1 inch is about the same as 2.5 cm. So 2 inches are roughly:
   a) 8 cm   b) 3 cm   c) 5 cm

2. 4 inches are roughly:
   a) 10 cm   b) 15 cm   c) 20 cm

3. 6 inches are roughly:
   a) 8 cm   b) 12 cm   c) 15 cm

4. 12 inches make 1 foot. How long is 1 foot in centimetres?
   a) roughly 20 cm   b) roughly 30 cm   c) roughly 50 cm

5. 100 cm make one 1 metre. Which of these is closest to 100 cm?
   a) 3 feet   b) 2 feet   c) 4 feet

DEFINITION

unit of measurement: Words like 'centimetre', 'litre', 'inch' or 'pound'.

B

1 **kilogram** weighs about the same as **2.5 pounds**.
So **2 kilos** weigh about the same as **5 pounds**.
Join the sacks that are roughly the same weight.

The short way to write 'pounds' is 'lb'. Like this: 6lb. You sometimes see 'pints' written as 'pt', like this: 5pt.

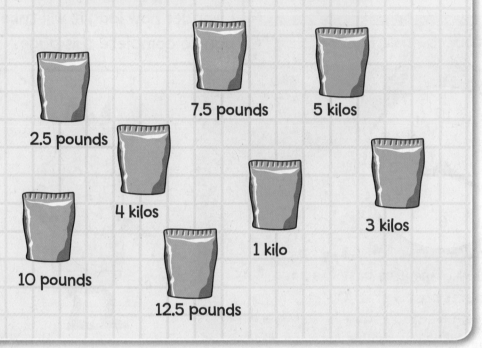

7.5 pounds

5 kilos

2.5 pounds

4 kilos

3 kilos

10 pounds

1 kilo

12.5 pounds

C

An old-fashioned pint is a little bit more than half a litre.
Join the bottles that show about the same amount.

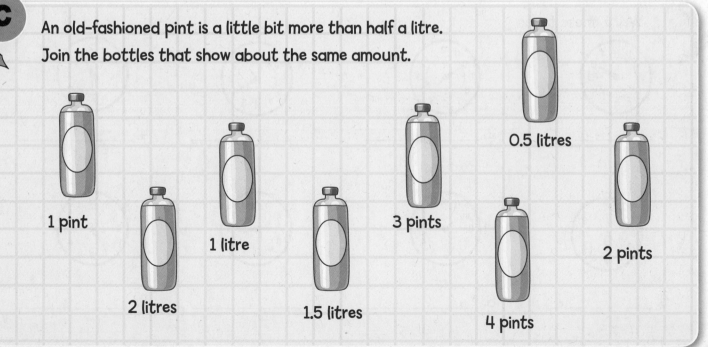

0.5 litres

1 pint

1 litre

3 pints

2 pints

2 litres

1.5 litres

4 pints

Time

There are 60 minutes in 1 hour. It takes 5 minutes for the minute hand to move from one marker to the next.

This shows the hour. It is past 3 o'clock.

This shows the number of minutes past the hour.
It is 40 minutes past 3 or 3.40.

I wonder how long it will take you to complete this page?

A Write these times.

1. _____

2. _____

3. _____

4. _____

5. _____

6. _____

7. _____

8. _____

B

Read these time problems. Write the answers.

1. A TV programme starts at 6.15 and lasts for half an hour.
   What time will it end? _____

2. Nathan gets up at 7 o'clock and leaves for school an hour later.
   What time does he leave for school? _____

3. A boat leaves at ten past one and returns at half-past one.
   How long was the boat at sea? _____

4. A cake takes 25 minutes to bake. It was put in the oven at 4 o'clock.
   When will it be ready? _____

5. Gemma is playing at the park. It is quarter to 12. She has to go home at 12.30.
   How much longer does she have to play? _____

C

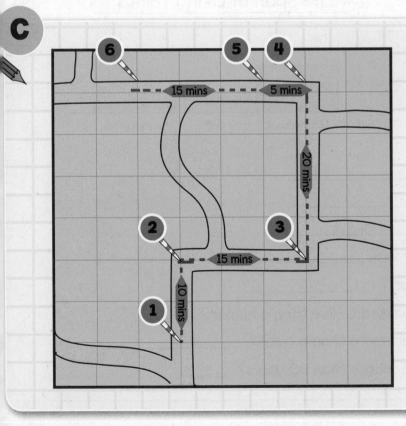

Look at the map showing the length of time a bus takes between each stop. Complete this bus timetable. Work out the time the bus will be at each stop.

Bus Stop	Time
1	9.05
2	
3	
4	
5	
6	

Handling data

Learning objective: to read the data in bar graphs

Data is information that has been collected.

A bar graph shows information in differently sized columns.

scale

axis

Number of visitors

50
40
30
20
10
0

label

Mon   Tue   Wed   Thur   Fri

Days of the week

Bar graphs look like bars. What do you think pie graphs look like?

A Answer these questions about the bar graph.

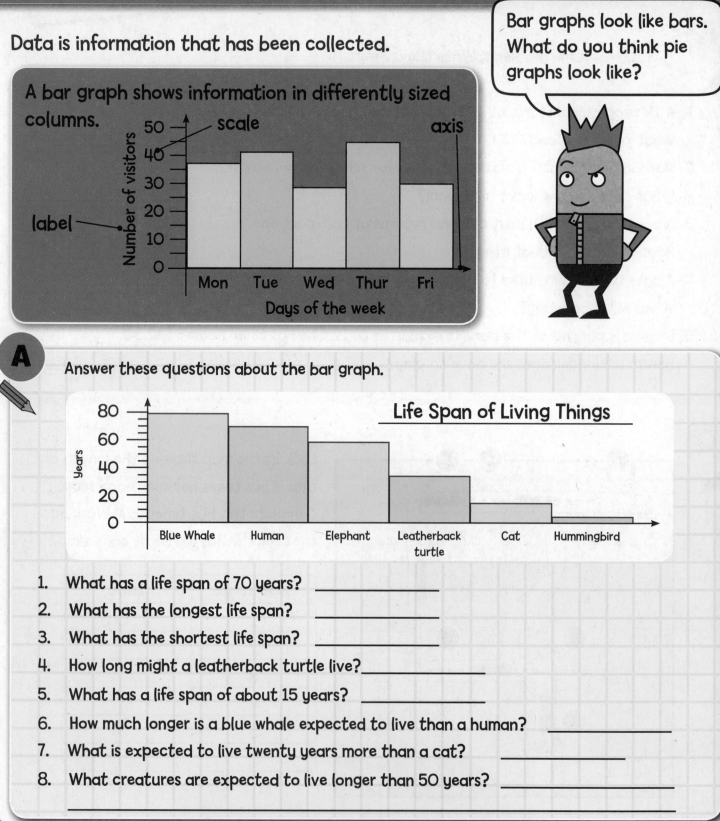

Life Span of Living Things

Years

80
60
40
20
0

Blue Whale   Human   Elephant   Leatherback turtle   Cat   Hummingbird

1. What has a life span of 70 years? _____

2. What has the longest life span? _____

3. What has the shortest life span? _____

4. How long might a leatherback turtle live? _____

5. What has a life span of about 15 years? _____

6. How much longer is a blue whale expected to live than a human? _____

7. What is expected to live twenty years more than a cat? _____

8. What creatures are expected to live longer than 50 years? _____
_____

B

This chart shows the favourite fruits of children in Class 3.

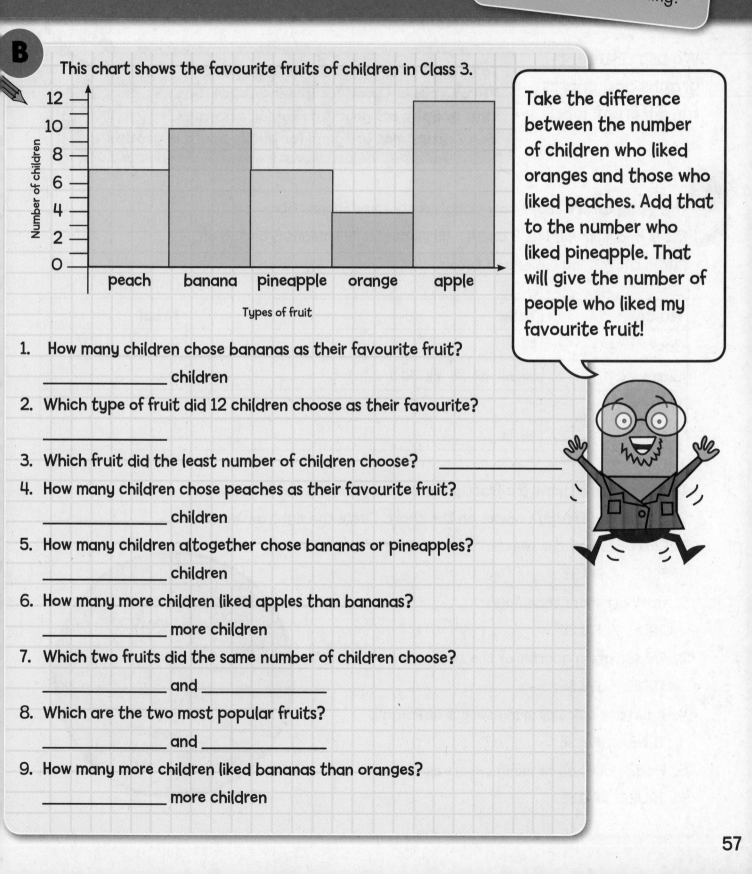

Take the difference between the number of children who liked oranges and those who liked peaches. Add that to the number who liked pineapple. That will give the number of people who liked my favourite fruit!

1. How many children chose bananas as their favourite fruit?

_____ children

2. Which type of fruit did 12 children choose as their favourite?

_____

3. Which fruit did the least number of children choose?   _____

4. How many children chose peaches as their favourite fruit?

_____ children

5. How many children altogether chose bananas or pineapples?

_____ children

6. How many more children liked apples than bananas?

_____ more children

7. Which two fruits did the same number of children choose?

_____ and _____

8. Which are the two most popular fruits?

_____ and _____

9. How many more children liked bananas than oranges?

_____ more children

Graphs and charts

Learning objective: to use different types of graph and chart

We use different graphs and charts for different jobs.

Tally charts are good for **keeping count**.
Pie charts are good for showing **fractions**.
Line graphs are good for showing **changes**.
Venn diagrams are good for putting data in **groups**.

A

This **tally chart** shows how many sweets some friends ate.

I, II, III and IIII mean 1, 2, 3 and 4.   ⊞ means 5, ⊞ I means 6 and so on.

Put in the missing tallies and totals.

Name	Tally	Total
Jack	⊞ III	8
Claire	⊞ ⊞ ⊞ ⊞ ⊞ ⊞ II	
Freddy		16
Anya	⊞ III	

This **pie chart** shows the fraction of sweets eaten by each friend.

Put Anya and Freddy's names on the chart. Circle the right answers.

1. Claire ate half the sweets.

   TRUE / FALSE

2. Jack ate more than Anya.

   TRUE / FALSE

3. Freddy ate a quarter of the sweets.

   TRUE / FALSE

4. Anya ate twice as many sweets as Freddy.

   TRUE / FALSE

5. Freddy ate half as many sweets as Claire.

   TRUE / FALSE

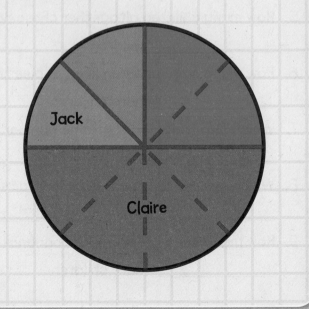

B

Jenny nibbled a chocolate bar.

This **line graph** shows how quickly she ate it.

1. How much of the bar was left after 15 seconds? _____

2. How much of the bar was left after 20 seconds? _____

3. Does Jenny's nibbling speed up or slow down? _____

4. If Jenny keeps nibbling at this speed, can she finish the bar in less than 30 seconds? _____

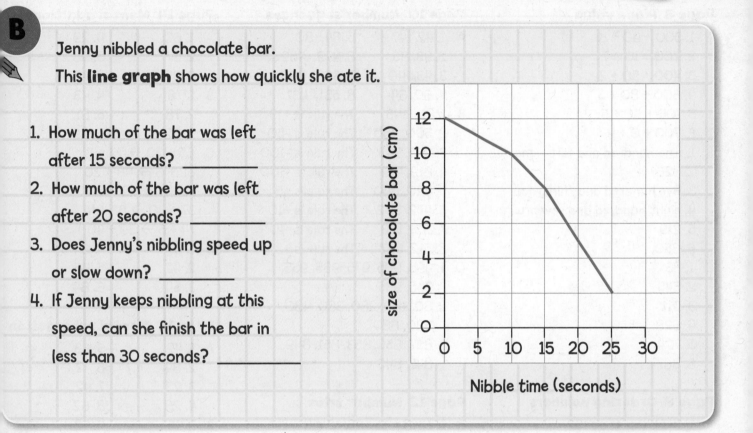

C

This **Venn diagram** shows the ice-creams that different people liked. Where the circles overlap, people liked more than one kind of ice-cream.

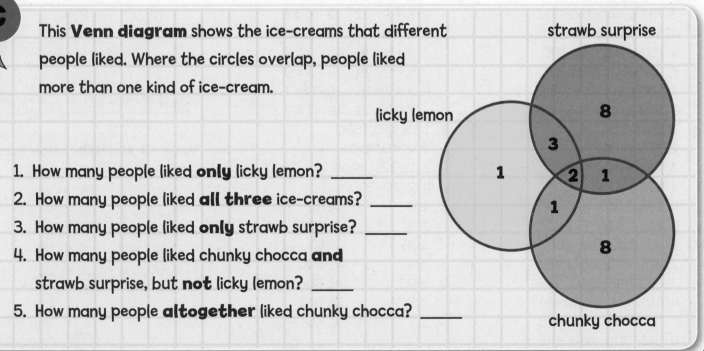

strawb surprise

licky lemon

chunky chocca

1. How many people liked **only** licky lemon? _____
2. How many people liked **all three** ice-creams? _____
3. How many people liked **only** strawb surprise? _____
4. How many people liked chunky chocca **and** strawb surprise, but **not** licky lemon? _____
5. How many people **altogether** liked chunky chocca? _____

59

Answers

Page 6 Place value

A 1. 300 + 90 + 8
   2. 200 + 10 + 7
   3. 400 + 50 + 2
   4. 600 + 80 + 3
   5. 100 + 60 + 5
   6. 700 + 0 + 9

B 1. nine hundred and forty-one
   2. 326
   3. five hundred and thirty-four
   4. eight hundred and seventy
   5. 219
   6. 650

C 1. 83
   2. 545
   3. 911
   4. 628
   5. 704
   6. 367

Page 8 Ordering numbers

A 1. 147 is less than 152.
   2. 476 is less than 479.
   3. 753 is more than 735.
   4. 521 is more than 381.
   5. 190 is less than 390.
   6. 214 is less than 244.
   7. 586 is more than 585.
   8. 592 is more than 497.

B 1. 264 > 254
   2. 328 < 431
   3. 190 > 119
   4. 536 > 523
   5. 708 < 807
   6. 655 > 635

C 1. 112, 125, 159, 191
   2. 278, 373, 387, 483
   3. 622, 645, 668, 739
   4. 410, 416, 460, 461
   5. 704, 743, 760, 778
   6. 195, 309, 459, 815

Page 10 Number sequences

A 1. 42, 47   5. 84, 80
   2. 93, 95   6. 479, 469
   3. 43, 40   7. 668, 768
   4. 60, 64   8. 531, 431

B 1. 85, 145   The rule is +15
   2. 500, 450   The rule is -50
   3. 943, 743   The rule is -100
   4. 619, 419   The rule is -100
   5. 820, 840   The rule is +5
   6. 472, 502   The rule is +10
   7. 113, 103   The rule is -10
   8. 512, 527   The rule is +3

C 1. 995, 985, 975, 965, 955,
      945, 935
   2. 80, 180, 280, 380, 480,
      580, 680
   3. 857, 855, 853, 851, 849,
      847, 845

Page 12 Number trios

A 1. 7 + 8 = 15   15 - 7 = 8
      8 + 7 = 15   15 - 8 = 7
   2. 6 + 6 = 12   12 - 6 = 6
      6 + 6 = 12   12 - 6 = 6
   3. 9 + 5 = 14   14 - 9 = 5
      5 + 9 = 14   14 - 5 = 9
   4. 9 + 7 = 16   16 - 9 = 7
      7 + 9 = 16   16 - 7 = 9

B 1. 15, 150, 1500
   2. 4, 40, 400
   3. 12, 120, 1200
   4. 2, 20, 200

C 1. 9   5. 60
   2. 8   6. 900
   3. 18   7. 50
   4. 4   8. 200

D 1. 90   4. 600
   2. 14   5. 700
   3. 7   6. 40

Page 14 Mental addition

A 1. 67   4. 29
   2. 57   5. 98
   3. 35   6. 78

B 1. 76   4. 43
   2. 78   5. 81
   3. 82   6. 89

C 55 + 20 → 72 + 3
   62 + 6 → 48 + 20
   71 + 8 → 29 + 50
   37 + 30 → 63 + 4
   74 + 5 → 39 + 40

D 1. 37   4. 64
   2. 42   5. 46
   3. 54   6. 84

Page 16 Mental subtraction

A 1. 42   5. 63
   2. 84   6. 12
   3. 23   7. 42
   4. 28   8. 62

B 1. 95   4. 42
   2. 52   5. 24
   3. 73   6. 41

C

1.

IN	56	78	27	49	15	64
OUT	52	74	23	45	11	60

2.

IN	65	91	42	77	59	83
OUT	35	61	12	47	29	53

Page 18 Multiplication facts

A 1. 24   4. 45
   2. 21   5. 30
   3. 27   6. 56

B 1. 35, 42   5. 9, 18
   2. 40, 48   6. 14, 28
   3. 60, 54   7. 16, 32
   4. 80, 72   8. 18, 36

C 1. 24   4. 2
  2. 27   5. 5
  3. 3   6. 3, she will
have some left over.

D

$$\boxed{2} \times \boxed{9} \to 18 \qquad \boxed{4} \times \boxed{7} \to 28$$
$$\times \quad \times \qquad\qquad \times \quad \times$$
$$\boxed{6} \times \boxed{9} \to 54 \qquad \boxed{9} \times \boxed{3} \to 27$$
$$\downarrow \quad \downarrow \qquad\qquad\quad \downarrow \quad \downarrow$$
$$12 \quad 81 \qquad\qquad 36 \quad 21$$

Page 20 Written addition

A 1. 200 + 70 + 15 = 285
  2. 100 + 70 + 18 = 188
  3. 200 + 70 + 11 = 281
B 1. 180   2. 244
  3. 296   4. 161
C 1. 93   4. 171
  2. 83   5. 294
  3. 72   6. 251
D 1. 90km   4. 185
  2. 67   5. 160
  3. 61   6. 174cm

Page 22 Written subtraction

A 1. 35   2. 27
  3. 26   4. 58
B 1. 5 + 10 = 15   2. 1 + 12 = 13
  3. 3 + 14 = 17   4. 4 + 5 = 9
C 1. 20   4. 51
  2. 27   5. 15
  3. 18   6. 29
D

a) 2	7	b) 1	c) 3	9
2	d) 3	5	6	e) 4
f) 4	1	g) 3	h) 1	5
6	i) 4	7	8	j) 8

Page 24 Multiplication

A 1. 56   2. 225
  3. 222   4. 174
B 1. 152   2. 184
  3. 156   4. 185
C 1. 172   4. 184
  2. 141   5. 204
  3. 171   6. 140
D 1. 192   4. 144
  2. 95km   5. 168 hours
  3. 210   6. 177

Page 26 Division

A 1. 9 r 3   4. 8 r 2
  2. 6 r 1   5. 5 r 5
  3. 7 r 2   6. 6 r 4
B 1. 28   6. 3
  2. 9   7. 6
  3. 6   8. 8
  4. 8   9. 7
  5. 3   10. 32
C 1. 11 teams
  2. 3 children
  3. 17 teams   1 left over
     8 teams   3 left over
     7 teams   0 left over
     5 teams   5 left over
     5 teams   0 left over
Challenge: 61

Page 28 Fractions of quantities

A 1. 5   2. 3   3. 9
  4. 3   5. 7
B 12 red, 4 yellow, 8 blue,
  6 large, 3 long
C 1. 7, 14   5. 7, 49
  2. 10, 30   6. 4, 28
  3. 3, 15   7. 11, 22
  4. 2, 16   8. 5, 25
Challenge: He has 32 sweets left.

Page 30 Decimals

A 1. 6.3   4. 18.5
  2. 0.9   5. 11.1
  3. 12.4

  1. $\frac{8}{10}$ 4. $20\frac{6}{10}$
  2. $7\frac{2}{10}$ 5. $4\frac{9}{10}$
  3. $16\frac{7}{10}$
B 1. 2   4. $\frac{2}{10}$
  2. 20   5. $\frac{2}{10}$
  3. $\frac{2}{10}$ 6. 2

C 7.5   8.1   8.7   9.7
  12.9   13.4   13.8   14.3

D 1. >   5. >
  2. <   6. >
  3. >   7. <
  4. <   8. <

Answers

Page 32 Using a calculator

A **ON** turns the calculator on and off.

is the display screen.

C is the cancel button.

+ is the button for adding.

− is the button for subtracting.

÷ is the button for dividing.

X is the button for multiplying.

= is the answer button.

. is the decimal point button.

 are the number buttons.

1. The largest figure you can make on most calculators is: 999,999,999
2. The smallest figure you can make on most calculators is: 0.00000001.

B 5, 10, 15.
Steps in 'make your own calculator trail' will vary but must produce the answer 20.

C 1. 3
2. 5
3. 2
4. 6
5. 9
The √ button always finds what number multiplied by itself makes your starting number.

Page 34 2-D shapes

A 1. quadrilateral, 2. octagon, 3. hexagon, 4. pentagon, 5. triangle, 6. hexagon

B 1. Hexagons - odd one out is a quadrilateral.
2. Quadrilaterals - odd one out is a pentagon.
3. Ovals - odd one out is a circle.

C Check all shapes are pentominoes.

Page 36 Symmetry

A Symmetrical → leaf, TV, ladder
Not symmetrical → car, cup, sock

B Check each shape drawn is an exact reflection.

C 1. M 4. U
2. B 5. 3
3. X

Challenge: DECK, CODE, HOOD, WHAT, TOW, HIM

Page 38 Angles

A Check instructions have been followed.

B Check estimated angles are within 5 degrees of these:
1. 150° 2. 110° 3. 90° 4. 45°
5. 30° 6. 130° 7. 70° 8. 90°

C Check all right angles are marked correctly.

D The order should be:
6 (30°), 4 (45°), 2 (60°),
1 (100°), 3 (120°), 5 (160°)

Challenge: 32

Page 40 3-D solids

A 1. cone 4. cuboid
2. sphere 5. cylinder
3. cube 6. prism

B 1. All cylinders. The odd one out is a cone.
2. All cubes. The odd one out is a sphere.
3. All cuboids. The odd one out is a prism.

C

Name of shape	cube	cuboid	prism
Total number of faces	6	6	5
Number of square and rectangle faces	6	6	3
Number of triangular faces	0	0	2

D 1. never 2. always 3. never 4. sometimes

Page 42 Measuring length

A Estimates should be within 1cm of the answers to section B.

B 1. 5cm 4. 7cm
2. 8cm 5. 10cm
3. 12cm 6. 3cm

C 1. 10cm 5. 14cm
2. 4cm 6. 3.5cm
3. 2.5cm 7. 6.5cm
4. 11cm 8. 8.5cm

Page 44 Measuring perimeter

A 1. 16m 4. 24m
2. 28m 5. 18m
3. 22m 6. 32m

B 1. l 3cm, h 1.5cm, p 9cm
2. l 4cm, h 1cm, p 10cm
3. l 1.5cm, h 1.5cm, p 6cm
4. l 2.5cm, h 3cm, p 11cm

5. l 4cm, h 1.5cm, p 11cm

6. l 2.5cm, h 1cm, p 7cm

C

Rectangle	length	add	height	Multiply total by 2	Perimeter
1	6m	+	2m	= 8 m → x 2	16m
2	8m	+	4m	= 12 m → x 2	24m
3	5m	+	5m	= 10 m → x 2	20m
4	7m	+	9m	= 16 m → x 2	32m
5	11m	+	1m	= 12 m → x 2	24m

Page 46 Measuring area

A 1. 9 square centimetres
2. 5 square centimetres
3. 7 square centimetres
4. 6 square centimetres
5. 10 square centimetres
6. 6 square centimetres

B 1. 8 square metres
2. 49 square metres
3. 16 square metres
4. 23 square metres
5. 25 square metres

C Check designs are all different and made from 8 squares.

Page 48 Measuring capacity

Challenge: Three 3-litre jugs and
two 4-litre jugs.

A 1. 80 ml   4. 50ml
2. 600ml   5. 200ml
3. 3 litres   6. 1.5 litres

B 1. 4   2. 2   3. 1   4. 2   5. 1

C 1. 2   4. 20
2. 10   5. 4
3. 4   6. 5

Page 50 Measuring weight

A 1. 1kg   4. 3 kg
2. 1 kg   5. ½ kg
3. ¼ kg   6. 1½ kg

B 1. 2kg   4. 6000g
2. 5000g   5. 9000g

3. 4kg   6. 3kg

C 1. 4kg   4. 7kg
2. 5½ kg   5. 8½ kg
3. 9 kg   6. 2½ kg

Challenge: 4kg

Page 52 Imperial measures

A 1. c) 5 cm   4. b) 30 cm
2. a) 10 cm   5. a) 3 feet
3. c) 15 cm

B 3 pounds = 7.5 kilos
1 pound = 2.5 kilos
4 pounds = 10 kilos
5 pounds = 12.5 kilos

C 1 pints and 0.5 litres
3 pints and 1.5 litres
4 pints and 2 litres
2 pints and 1 litre

Page 54 Time

Answers may be given as digital
(12.10) or in the 'o'clock' format.

A 1. 2.10   5. 7.30
2. 4.50   6. 10.15
3. 1.20   7. 3.45
4. 6.05   8. 8.35

B 1. 6.45
2. 8 o'clock
3. 20 minutes
4. 4.25
5. 45 minutes

C 1. 9.05   4. 9.50
2. 9.15   5. 9.55
3. 9.30   6. 10.10

Page 56 Handling data

A 1. human 2. blue whale
3. hummingbird 4. 35 years
5. cat 6. 10 years
7. leatherback turtle

8. elephant, human and blue whale

B 1. 10 2. apple 3. orange 4. 7
5. 17 6. 2 7. peach and pineapple 8. apple and banana
9. 6

Page 58 Graphs and charts

A

Name	Tally	Total
Jack	ⅢⅢ III	8
Claire	ⅢⅢ ⅢⅢ ⅢⅢ ⅢⅢ ⅢⅢ ⅢⅢ II	32
Freddy	ⅢⅢ ⅢⅢ ⅢⅢ I	16
Anya	ⅢⅢ III	8

1. TRUE
2. FALSE
3. TRUE
4. FALSE
5. TRUE

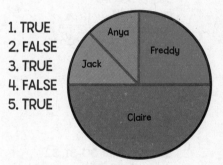

B 1. 8 cm
2. 5 cm
3. it speeds up
4. yes

C 1. 1 person
2. 2 people
3. 8 people
4. 1 person
5. 12 people (8 + 1 + 2 + 1 = 12)

Index